AWARD EDITION

HOUGHTON MIFFLIN

The
Literature
Experience

READING

Celebrate Reading with us!

COME ONE, COME ALL

Senior Author
John J. Pikulski

*Senior Coordinating
Author*
J. David Cooper

*Senior Consulting
Author*
William K. Durr

Coordinating Authors
Kathryn H. Au
M. Jean Greenlaw
Marjorie Y. Lipson
Susan E. Page
Sheila W. Valencia
Karen K. Wixson

Authors
Rosalinda B. Barrera
Edwina Bradley
Ruth P. Bunyan
Jacqueline L. Chaparro
Jacqueline C. Comas
Alan N. Crawford
Robert L. Hillerich
Timothy G. Johnson
Jana M. Mason
Pamela A. Mason
William E. Nagy
Joseph S. Renzulli
Alfredo Schifini

Senior Advisor
Richard C. Anderson

Advisors
Christopher J. Baker
Charles Peters
MaryEllen Vogt

HOUGHTON MIFFLIN COMPANY   BOSTON
Atlanta   Dallas   Geneva, Illinois   Palo Alto   Princeton   Toronto

THEME 1

8

Growing Up

🏵 12 Clean Your Room, Harvey Moon!
by Pat Cummings

🏵 44 Best Friends *by Steven Kellogg*

🏵 58 Ronald Morgan Goes to Bat
by Patricia Reilly Giff

POETRY
🏵 42 Whistles *by Dorothy Aldis*
🏵 43 Grandma's Baby Pictures *by Beth P. Wilson*
🏵 69 A Year Later *by Mary Ann Hoberman*

📖

THEME BOOKS
🏵 Molly and the Slow Teeth *by Pat Ross*
🏵 I Speak English for My Mom *by Muriel Stanek*

MEET THE POET
🏵 *Nikki Giovanni*
73 The Dragonfly
74 mommies
74 the drum
75 Covers

🏵 Award Winner

76

Tomie dePaola

79 The Art Lesson
by Tomie dePaola

96 Now One Foot, Now the Other
by Tomie dePaola

114 Strega Nona's Magic Lessons
by Tomie dePaola

POETRY
138 The Secret Place
by Tomie dePaola

THEME BOOKS
The Quicksand Book
by Tomie dePaola
The Legend of the Bluebonnet
by Tomie dePaola

THEME 3

142 **Aesop's Fables**

🎗 146 The Tortoise and the Hare
retold by Janet Stevens

164 The Lion and the Mouse
a play retold by Robert Hoffer

🎗 180 Pulín and Miga *from* Pupurupú
retold by Sabine R. Ulibarrí
translated from Spanish

POETRY
🎗 158 The Tortoise and the Hare
retold by Tom Paxton

THEME BOOKS
🎗 Once in a Wood: Ten Tales from Aesop
by Eve Rice
🎗 The Empty Pot   *by Demi*

THEME 4

196

IN and OUT of TROUBLE

🏵 200 Nessa's Fish   *by Nancy Luenn*

🏵 226 Curious George Gets a Medal
          by H. A. Rey

🏵 246 Tye May and the Magic Brush
          by Molly Garrett Bang

P O E T R Y
🏵 244 The Muddle   *by Marchette Chute*
245 Lost at the Zoo   *by Ilo Orleans*

T H E M E   B O O K S
🏵 Mouse Soup   *by Arnold Lobel*
Not Just Any Ring   *by Danita Ross Haller*

READING SCIENCE
264 Polar Bears

G L O S S A R Y
272

Growing Up

As you grow up, you get bigger, taller, and stronger. You also learn new things and do new things. Every day, in some way, you grow and change.

In this book, you will read stories about boys and girls just like you. They too are growing up.

Contents

Clean Your Room, Harvey Moon! 12
written and illustrated by Pat Cummings

Best Friends 44
written and illustrated by Steven Kellogg

Ronald Morgan Goes to Bat 58
by Patricia Reilly Giff
with illustrations by Susanna Natti

CLEAN YOUR ROOM, HARVEY MOON!

Written and Illustrated by Pat Cummings

On Saturday morning at ten to nine
Harvey Moon was eating toast,
Waiting for the cartoon show
That he enjoyed the most.

With only minutes left to go,
He heard the voice of DOOM.
"Today, young man," his mother said,
"Is the day you clean your room!"

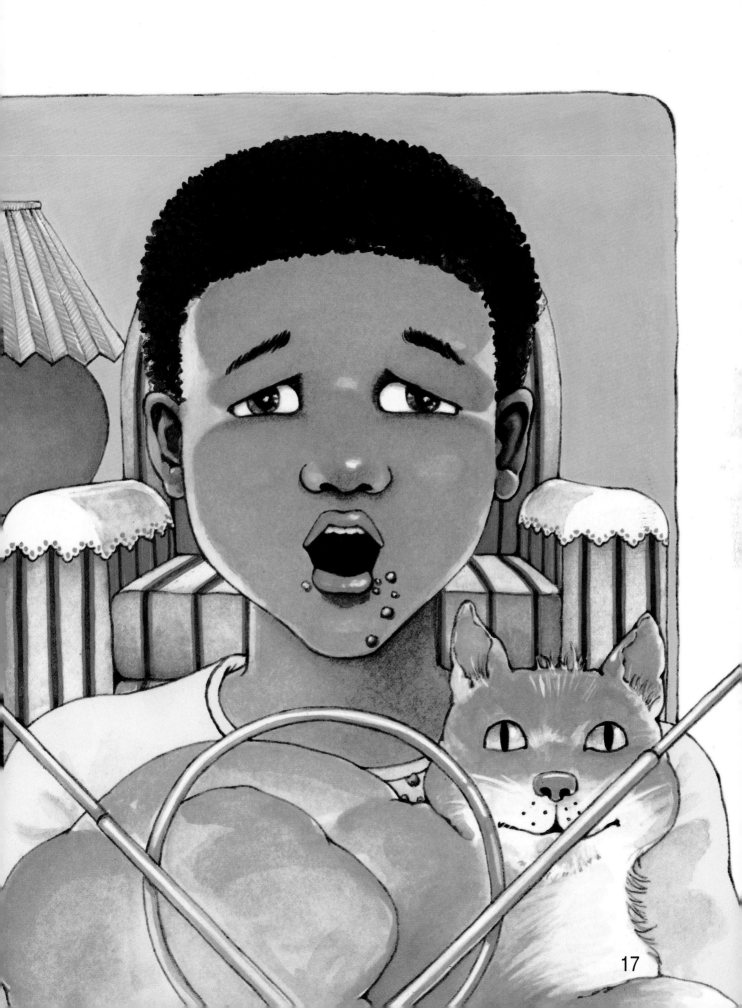

"Not nowwww . . ." moaned Harvey,
Red in the face.
"I'll miss 'Rotten Ed'
And 'Invaders from Space'!"
"Right this second!" she ordered,
And gave him the broom.
Harvey marched angrily
Up to his room.

It really didn't seem
Messy at all.
First he'd throw his dirty clothes
Out in the hall.
Under the bed was
An ice cream-smeared shirt,
Jeans that had what Mom called
"Ground-in dirt. . . ."

Two towels and swim trunks
That seemed to be wet,
Three socks he sniffed
And found weren't dirty yet.
Under the dresser was a lump
Warm and gray,
That he didn't recognize
So he put it away.

The floor of the closet had clumps
Hard and dirty
Of T-shirts and sweatshirts. . . .
IT WAS TEN-THIRTY!
Harvey panicked then thought,
"I should be through soon,
I'll eat lunch while I watch
'Creature Zero' at noon."

Grabbing marbles and crayons and
Flat bottle caps,
Two of his own special
Lightning bug traps,
The softball he couldn't find
Last Saturday,
One toothbrush, one helmet . . .
He put them away.

"I'll clear out these toys
And then I'll be done,
'Ken's Kung Fu Korner'
Will be on at one. . . ."
Under his desk were some comics
All icky
From something inside
That was dripping and sticky.

He found library books
He'd forgotten he had,
His skates from Aunt Sarah,
His bow tie from dad,
He found a caboose
That was missing its train,
A whistle, paintbrushes,
A map of the brain.

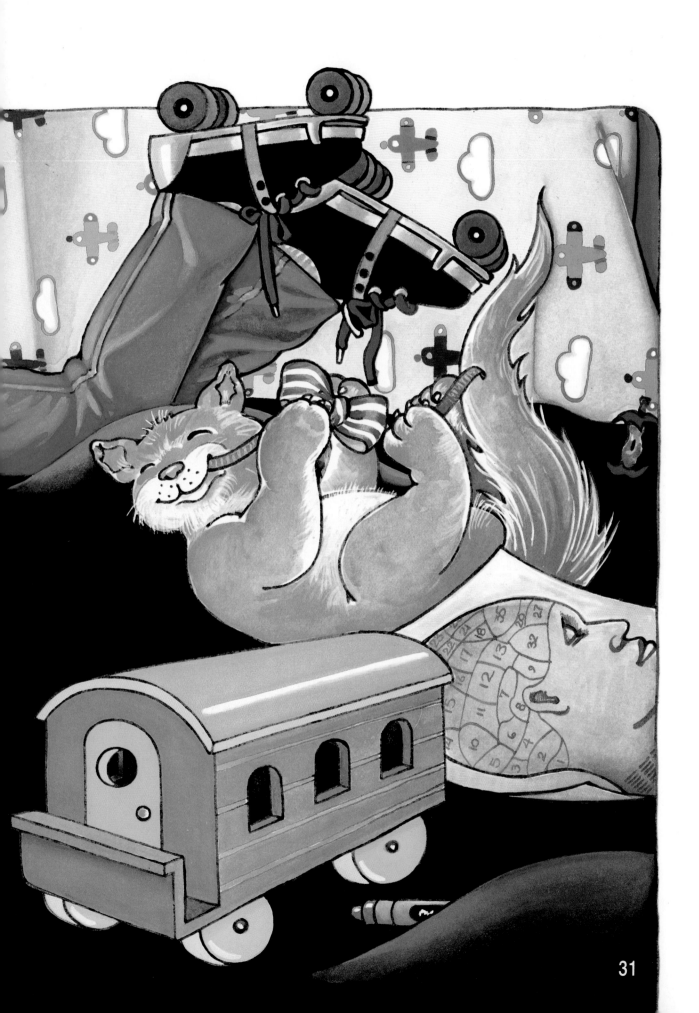

He found sneakers and card games
Up under the bed,
Goggles, flippers, and a grasshopper
. . . dead,
A long-lost cookie
All fuzzy and gray,
Plastic cars, boats, and planes,
And he put them away.

33

33

Just then Harvey happened
To notice the clock.
"IT'S ALMOST TWO!!" Harvey shouted.
He went into shock.
"I missed 'Caveman Capers'
On channel nine. . . .
I'm starving! I'm tired!
This room looks fine!"

He put up his bathrobe,
His bat, and football,
With a few other things
Then ran down the hall,
Shouting, "Mom, I'm finished!"
Harvey put back the broom.
His mother stepped cautiously
Into his room.

"I'm really amazed," his mom said.
Harvey beamed.
He could watch TV now. He was through,
So it seemed.
"I fixed you some lunch," she said.
"When you are done,
You and I will get started
On lump number one!"

THE END?

A ROOMFUL OF CLUES

Get together with a friend and choose five or six things that are part of the mess in Harvey Moon's room. Think of them as clues. What do they tell you about Harvey Moon? What does he like to do? Give your report to the class.

About the Author and Illustrator

Pat Cummings started out as an illustrator of books by other authors. Then she began to illustrate books she wrote herself.

When Pat Cummings writes, she tries to see things through the eyes of her characters. Sometimes she imagines the room one of her characters might live in, looking for clues that can tell her more about the person who lives there.

Another Pat Cummings book you may enjoy reading is *Jimmy Lee Did It*, about an imaginary friend who always gets the blame.

Whistles

I want to learn to whistle.
I've always wanted to.
I fix my mouth to do it but
The whistle won't come through.

I think perhaps it's stuck, and so
I try it once again.
Can people swallow whistles?
Where is my whistle then?

Dorothy Aldis

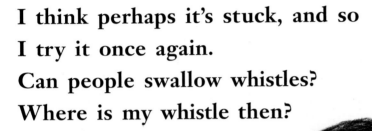

Grandma's
Baby Pictures

When I go visiting with Grandma
she likes to show people my
baby pictures on her bracelet.
Her friends say, "I remember
when you were a baby." I don't
like that. It makes me feel shy.

Beth P. Wilson

BEST FRIENDS

Story and pictures by

STEVEN KELLOGG

Louise Jenkins and I love horses, but we aren't allowed to have real ones.

I said, "Let's pretend that a stallion named Golden Silverwind lives in a stable between our houses." Louise loved the idea.

At school we pushed our desks together. And we played on the same team. At lunch we shared our chocolate milk. Chocolate is Louise's favorite, and it's mine too.

After school we pretended that we rode Golden Silverwind. Our magic witch hats gave us the power to make our neighborhood anything we wanted it to be.

And after dark, when it seemed to be haunted, we weren't scared as long as we were together. We were best friends.

Summer came, and so did Louise's aunt and uncle. They took her to a mountain resort for a vacation. Louise told me that she didn't want to go. "It will be awful," she said. "And I'll miss you every day."

When she left, our neighborhood turned into a lonely desert. If only Louise would be able to escape.

I even wished she'd get a contagious disease so they'd have to let her come home.

★

I wouldn't be afraid of catching it. I'd nurse her back to health with chocolate milk.

I missed her so much! I wished that Golden Silverwind and I could rescue her!

Finally I got a postcard. It said:

Dear Kathy,
   This place is terrific. Yesterday I saw three deer behind the lodge. There are lots of kids my age, and Aunt Pat and Uncle Bart take us camping on Pine Cone Peak. I hope you're having fun too.
   Love from your friend,
   Louise

Later I heard Mrs. Jenkins say that Louise had made lots of new friends and was having the best summer of her life.

It wasn't fair. She wasn't lonely like me. She wasn't missing me at all.

Louise Jenkins was a traitor! She was my *worst* friend.

I wished that a volcanic eruption would blast Pine Cone Peak into pebbles.

Mom told me not to be jealous of Louise's new friends.

Later she said, "I heard that the house across the street has been sold. Maybe there'll be someone your age in the new family."

I prayed for fifty kids my age. Fifty new best friends with *real* horses!

When the moving man came, I asked him, "How many people in the new family?"

He said, "One."

I asked if it was someone my age.

He said, "Nope, it's Mr. Jode. He's seventy-two."

This was the worst summer of my life! The new family was one old man!

Mom said we should be good neighbors, and she sent me to invite Mr. Jode for a cookout.

When he saw my witch hat he said, "I wish you'd use your magic powers to help me find good homes for the new puppies that Sarah is expecting."

I ran home to ask Mom if I could have one. She said yes.

I couldn't wait to have a puppy of my own. And if Louise Jenkins wanted to play with it after she got back from Pine Cone Peak I'd say "NEVER!" That would fix her.

Mr. Jode and I talked about how much fun it would be when the puppies were born. I told him I wanted a spotted one just like Sarah.

"The first spotted one will be yours," he promised.

One day Mrs. Jenkins showed up and said, "I understand that your dog is expecting puppies. I'd like to reserve one for my daughter, Louise."

I couldn't stand to think of Louise having one of Sarah's puppies. I told Mr. Jode that I would keep all of them.

Mr. Jode said, "Three years ago Sarah had eight puppies in one litter. Would your mother want that many dogs?"

50

I had to admit that eight dogs would drive my mom crazy.

Mr. Jode asked me if I was afraid that Louise wouldn't give her puppy a good home. I had to admit that she would.

A week later Louise came back. Her mother had already told her that we were both getting puppies, and she was all excited about us raising them together.

Next she started talking about all the campouts on Pine Cone Peak, and how her uncle and aunt had already planned a return trip for the following summer.

I pretended to be very interested in my book.

Then she told me that she was glad to be home, and that she had missed me very much.

She had brought me a red Pine Cone Peak sweatshirt, a sparrow's feather, a rock collection, and a whistle on a lanyard that she had woven herself.

I told her how much I'd missed her. But I didn't tell her how mad I had been.

I took Louise to meet my new friends. I knew that they would all like each other, and they did. I said, "Aren't Sarah's spots beautiful? I'm going to get the first puppy that looks like her."

A few nights later Mr. Jode called to say that Sarah was having her puppies.

By the time we arrived, one puppy had already
been born. It was brown. Mr. Jode handed him to
Louise saying, "When he grows up, he'll look just like
Sarah's mother."

Sarah went to sleep. Mr. Jode and Louise made
hot chocolate and tried to think of a name for her
puppy. I couldn't wait for mine to be born.

Sarah slept for hours. Finally Mr. Jode said, "It
looks like there's only one puppy this time. Sarah has
never had such a small litter before."

I felt awful.

It wasn't fair! Louise got to spend the whole
summer camping on Pine Cone Peak, and now she had
Sarah's only puppy.

Louise said, "I think the brown puppy should belong to both of us. We could name him Golden Silverwind."

Mr. Jode said, "I'll build him a dog house between your houses."

"And Sarah and I will help with his training."

When I got home, I kept thinking how lucky I was to have a special friend like Louise. I was already worried about how much I would miss her when she went away next summer.

But at least this time when she's camping on Pine Cone Peak I'll have Golden Silverwind all to myself.

THE END

★

Sharing Problems
What Would You Do?

Louise and Kathy solved their problem by building a dog house between their two yards.

With a partner, discuss how you might solve each of these problems.

1. Your two best friends invite you to their birthday parties. The parties are on the same day at the same time. What will you do?

2. Your best friend does not like your new friend. What will you do?

About the Author and Illustrator

Steven Kellogg loved making up stories for his little sisters. He would sit between his sisters and draw pictures to go with the stories as he told them. That is how Steven Kellogg started his career as a writer and artist. Since then he has written and illustrated over fifty books!

Here are some other Steven Kellogg books you might enjoy:

Can I Keep Him? Arnold wants a pet, but his mother doesn't like cats, dogs, or tigers.

The Mysterious Tadpole When a little tadpole gets too big for the bathtub, it's time for a clever solution.

DID YOU KNOW ?

As you get older and grow up, your body grows up too! Here are some interesting facts about your body that will grow on you.

SKINTIGHT

Almost every four weeks, a new layer of skin replaces the old layer of skin.

WHAT A BRAIN!

Babies have brains that weigh about three ounces. Adults have brains that weigh about three pounds. That's sixteen times bigger!

MUSCLE-BOUND

When you smile you use fourteen muscles.

HARD AS NAILS

When summer comes your nails will grow faster than they did in winter. Fingernails grow four times faster than toenails. If you are right-handed your nails will grow faster on your right hand. If you're left-handed the nails on your left hand will grow faster.

HAIR-RAISING

Dark hair grows faster than light-colored hair. No one knows why.

COUNT YOUR BONES

When we are born we have 300 bones. As we grow older, some of these bones grow together. That's why adults have only 206 bones.

Ronald Morgan Goes to Bat

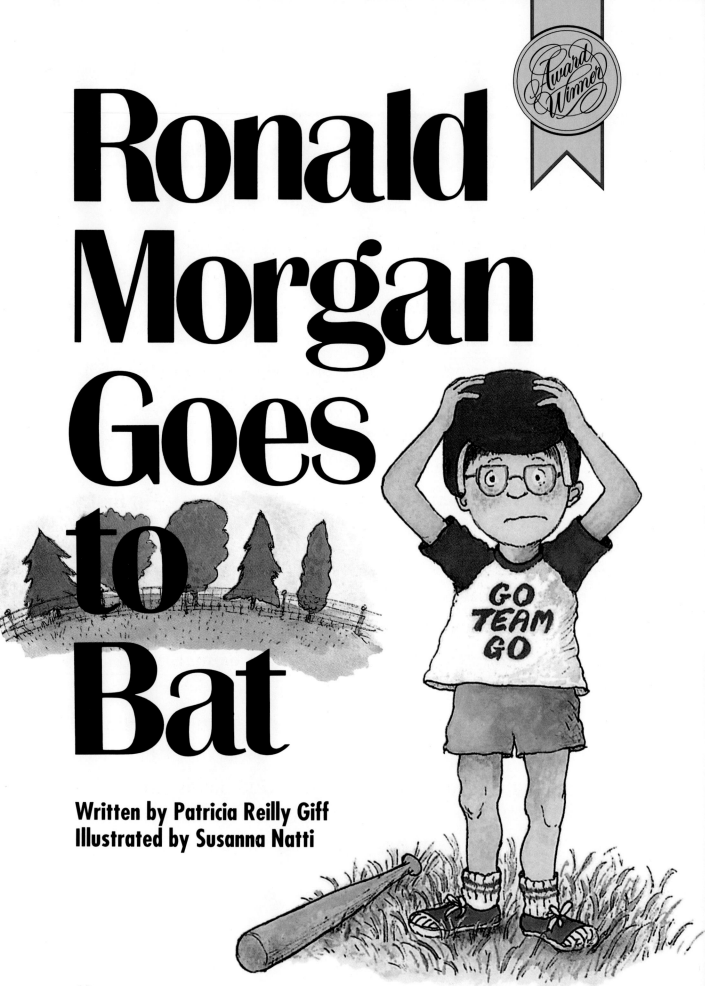

GO TEAM GO

Written by Patricia Reilly Giff
Illustrated by Susanna Natti

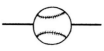

Baseball started today. Mr. Spano said everyone could play.

"Even me?" I asked.

And Tom said, "You're letting Ronald Morgan play? He can't hit, he can't catch. He can't do anything."

Mr. Spano looked at me. "Everyone," he said.

"Yahoo!" I yelled.

I pulled on my red and white shirt, the one that says GO TEAM GO, and ran outside to the field.

"Two things," Mr. Spano told us. "Try hard, and keep your eye on the ball."

Then it was time to practice. Michael was up first. He smacked the ball with the bat. The ball flew across the field.

"Good," said Mr. Spano.

"Great, Slugger!" I yelled. "We'll win every game."

It was my turn next. I put on the helmet, and stood at home plate.

"Ronald Morgan," said Rosemary. "You're holding the wrong end of the bat."

Quickly I turned it around. I clutched it close to the end.

Whoosh went the first ball.

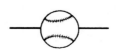

Whoosh went the second one.

Wham went the third. It hit me in the knee.

"Are you all right?" asked Michael.

But I heard Tom say, "I knew it. Ronald Morgan's the worst."

At snack time, we told Miss Tyler about the team.

"I don't hit very well," I said.

And Rosemary said, "The ball hits him instead."

Everybody laughed, even me.

I shook my head. "I hope it doesn't happen again."

Miss Tyler gave me some raisins. "You have to hit the ball before it hits you," she said.

We played every day. I tried hard, but the ball came fast. I closed my eyes and swung.

"If only he could hit the ball once," Rosemary said. And Billy shook his head. I couldn't tell them I was afraid of the ball.

"Go team go," I whispered.

One day, the team sat on the grass. We watched the third grade play. They were big, they were strong, they were good. Johnny hit a home run, and Joy tagged a man out.

"We'll never hit like that," said Tom.

And Rosemary said, "We'll never catch like that either."

But I said, "Our team is the best."

Mr. Spano nodded. "That's the spirit, Ronald."

Mr. Spano told us, "Now we'll run the bases. Rosemary, you can go first."

Rosemary went fast. She raced for first base.

"Terrific, Speedy!" I yelled.

"Let me go next," I said. "I can do that, too."

But the field was muddy. My sneaker came off.

Jimmy said, "That kid's running bases the wrong way."

And Tom yelled, "Ronald Morgan. You're heading for third base."

The next day, we worked on catching. I was out in left field. While I waited, I found a stick, and started to scratch out the mud. I wrote G for go. I wrote G for great. Our team is the best, I thought. Then I wrote H for hit. H for home run. If only I could do that.

Just then I heard yelling. Someone had hit the ball. "Catch it, Ronald!" Tom shouted.

I put down the stick. I put up my mitt. Too late. The ball sailed into the trees.

Mr. Spano took us for ice cream. "You deserve it for trying," he said. "Our team is really good."

I had a chocolate cone. Michael's a slugger, I thought. And Rosemary can really run. But I'm still afraid of the ball.

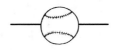

On the way home, we saw some kids playing ball. "Want to hit a few?" Michael asked.

I shook my head. "Maybe I won't play ball anymore."

Michael said, "We need you. You have spirit. You help the team feel good."

"But how can we win?" I asked. "I can't even hit the ball."

I saw my father and ran to catch up. "See you, Michael," I said.

My father asked, "How's the champ?"

"I'm the worst," I said.

"I was the worst, too," said my father. "But then . . ."

"What?"

My father laughed. "I stopped closing my eyes when I swung."

"Maybe that's what I do."

"How about a little practice?" he asked.

We went into the yard. My father threw me some balls. I missed the first one . . . I missed the second. And then . . .

I opened my eyes and swung. *Crack* went the ball. "Ouch!" went my father. "You hit me in the knee."

"Home run!" yelled my mother.

"Sorry," I said. "Hey, I did it!"

My father rubbed his knee. "You certainly did," he said.

I ran to pick up the ball. "See you later," I said.

My father smiled. "Where are you going?"

I grabbed the bat. "Some kids are playing ball. I think I'll hit a few."

I looked back. "And you know what else? I guess I'll stay on the team. I have spirit . . . and sometimes I can hit the ball. Mike was right. I think they need me."

Three Cheers for the Home Team!

Ronald Morgan was not the best baseball player, but he had a lot of team spirit. He always cheered for his team. Make up a cheer for Ronald's team. You may want to make it rhyme like this one:

COME ON, ROSEMARY, RUN, RUN, RUN!
ONE MORE BASE AND THE GAME IS DONE!

Now choose a partner, and act out your cheer. Act it out with a lot of team spirit!

About the Author

Patricia Reilly Giff loves to read. "I spent most of my childhood with a book in my hands," she has said. "After school, I'd sit in the kitchen leaning against the warm radiator, dreaming over a story." Patricia Reilly Giff has written over fifteen books, including *Watch Out, Ronald Morgan.*

About the Illustrator

By the time she was eight, Susanna Natti knew that she would be an illustrator. She grew up on Cape Ann, on the coast of Massachusetts, where many authors and artists live. Her mother is a writer of children's books.

Other books Susanna Natti has illustrated are *The Downtown Fairy Godmother* by Charlotte Pomerantz, and all of the Cam Jansen mysteries by David Adler.

A Year Later

Last summer I couldn't swim at all;
I couldn't even float!
I had to use a rubber tube
Or hang on to a boat;
I had to sit on shore
While everybody swam.
But now it's this summer
And I can!

Mary Ann Hoberman

GROW WITH THESE BOOKS!

I Speak English for My Mom
by Muriel Stanek

Lupe's mother can only speak Spanish. But she will need to learn English in order to find a new job.

Molly and the Slow Teeth
by Pat Ross

Molly thinks she'll never lose her baby teeth, so she tries to fool the tooth fairy.

Bigmama's
by Donald Crews

The author remembers the summers he and his family spent at his grandmother's house.

The Josefina Story Quilt
by Eleanor Coerr

When her family goes to California in a covered wagon, Faith takes along her pet hen, Josefina.

Yagua Days
by Cruz Martel

Adan thinks rainy days are terrible days. Then he travels to Puerto Rico and discovers that rainy days are yagua days!

Award Winner

Meet
Nikki Giovanni

Nikki Giovanni likes to write poems about things she remembers from when she was a child. She wrote a poem called "knoxville, tennessee" about summer in the city where she grew up. It begins:

I always like summer
best
you can eat fresh corn
from daddy's garden
and okra
and greens
and cabbage
and lots of
barbecue
and buttermilk
and homemade ice-cream
at the church picnic

In her two books of poems for children, *Spin a Soft Black Song* and *Vacation Time,* Nikki Giovanni has written about soap bubbles and sunbeams, taking naps and getting ready for trips, sitting in the mud and walking through a strawberry patch.

She has said that she writes both for children and for adults who are children at heart.

THE DRAGONFLY

A dragonfly sat
    on my nose
I wish it had sat
    on my toes
I guess nobody
    ever knows
Where a dragonfly will sit

73

MOMMIES

MOMMIES

make you brush your teeth
and put your old clothes on
and clean the room
and call you from the playground
and fuss at daddies and uncles
and tuck you in at night
and kiss you

THE DRUM

daddy says the world is
a drum tight and hard
and i told him
i'm gonna beat
out my own rhythm

COVERS

Glass covers windows
    to keep the cold away
Clouds cover the sky
    to make a rainy day

Nighttime covers
    all the things that creep
Blankets cover me
    when I'm asleep

•TOMIE dePAOLA•

Tomie dePaola

Some people write wonderful
stories. Other people draw
great pictures. Tomie dePaola
does both. In this book you will
read three of the many stories
he has written and illustrated.
One of the stories is funny,
one is serious, and one is almost
true. After each story, you will
also read a special message that
Tomie dePaola wrote just for you.

Table of Contents

The Art Lesson
written and illustrated by Tomie dePaola
79

Now One Foot, Now the Other
written and illustrated by Tomie dePaola
96

Strega Nona's Magic Lessons
written and illustrated by Tomie dePaola
114

The Art Lesson

written and illustrated by Tomie dePaola

Tommy knew he wanted to be an artist when he grew up. He drew pictures everywhere he went. It was his favorite thing to do.

His friends had favorite things to do, too. Jack collected all kinds of turtles. Herbie made huge cities in his sandbox. Jeannie, Tommy's best friend, could do cartwheels and stand on her head.

But Tommy drew
and drew and drew.

His twin cousins,
who were already grown
up, were in art school

learning to be real artists. They told him not to copy
and to practice, practice, practice. So, he did.

Tommy put his pictures up on the walls of his half of the bedroom.

His mom put them up all around the house.

His dad took them to the barber shop where he worked.

Tom and Nana, Tommy's Irish grandfather and grandmother, had his pictures in their grocery store.

Nana-Fall-River, his Italian grandmother, put one in a special frame on the table next to the photograph of Aunt Clo in her wedding dress.

Once Tommy took a flashlight and a pencil under the covers and drew pictures on his sheets. But when his mom changed the sheets on Monday and found them, she said, "No more drawing on the sheets, Tommy."

His mom and dad were having a new house built, so Tommy drew pictures of what it would look like when it was finished.

When the walls were up, one of the carpenters gave Tommy a piece of bright blue chalk.

Tommy took the chalk and drew beautiful pictures all over the unfinished walls.

But, when the painters came, his dad said, "That's it, Tommy. No more drawing on the walls."

Tommy couldn't wait to go to kindergarten. His brother, Joe, told him there was a real art teacher who came to the school to give ART LESSONS!

"When do we have our art lessons?" Tommy asked the kindergarten teacher.

"Oh, you won't have your art lessons until next year," said Miss Bird. "But, we *are* going to paint pictures tomorrow."

It wasn't much fun.

The paint was awful and the paper got all wrinkly. Miss Bird made the paint by pouring different colored powders into different jars and mixing them with water. The paint didn't stick to the paper very well and it cracked.

If it was windy when Tommy carried his picture home, the paint blew right off the paper.

"At least you get more than one piece of paper in kindergarten," his brother, Joe, said. "When the art teacher comes, you only get one piece."

Tommy knew that the art teacher came to the school every other Wednesday. He could tell she was an artist because she wore a blue smock over her dress and she always carried a big box of thick colored chalks.

Once, Tommy and Jeannie looked at the drawings that were hung up in the hallway. They were done by the first graders.

"Your pictures are much better," Jeannie told Tommy. "Next year when we have real art lessons, you'll be the best one!"

Tommy could hardly wait. He practiced all summer. Then, on his birthday, which was right after school began, his mom and dad gave him a box of sixty-four Crayola crayons. Regular boxes of crayons had red, orange, yellow, green, blue, violet, brown and black. This box had so many other colors: blue-violet, turquoise, red-orange, pink and even gold, silver and copper.

"Class," said Miss Landers, the first-grade teacher, "next month, the art teacher will come to our room, so on Monday instead of Singing, we will practice using our crayons."

On Monday, Tommy brought his sixty-four crayons to school. Miss Landers was not pleased.

"Everyone must use the same crayons," she said. "SCHOOL CRAYONS!"

School crayons had only the same old eight colors.

As Miss Landers passed them out to the class, she said, "These crayons are school property, so do not break them, peel off the paper, or wear down the points."

"How am I supposed to practice being an artist with SCHOOL CRAYONS?" Tommy asked Jack and Herbie.

"That's enough, Tommy," Miss Landers said. "And I want you to take those birthday crayons home with you and leave them there."

And Joe was right.
They only got ONE
piece of paper.

Finally, the day
of the art lesson came.
Tommy could hardly
sleep that night.

The next morning, he hid the box of sixty-four
crayons under his sweater and went off to school.
He was ready!

The classroom door opened and in walked the art
teacher. Miss Landers said, "Class, this is Mrs. Bowers,
the art teacher. Patty, who is our paper monitor this
week, will give out one piece of paper to each of you.
And remember, don't ruin it because it is the only piece
you'll get. Now, pay attention to Mrs. Bowers."

"Class," Mrs. Bowers began, "because Thanksgiving is not too far away, we will learn to draw a Pilgrim man, a Pilgrim woman and a turkey. Watch carefully and copy me."

Copy? COPY? Tommy knew that *real* artists didn't copy. This was terrible. This was supposed to be a real art lesson. He folded his arms and just sat there.

"Now what's the matter?" Miss Landers asked. Tommy looked past her and spoke right to Mrs. Bowers.

"I'm going to be an artist when I grow up and my cousins told me that real artists don't copy. And besides, Miss Landers won't let me use my own sixty-four Crayola crayons."

"Well, well," Mrs. Bowers said. "What are we going to do?" She turned to Miss Landers and they whispered together. Miss Landers nodded.

"Now, Tommy," Mrs. Bowers said. "It wouldn't be fair to let you do something different from the rest of the class.

"But, I have an idea. If you draw the Pilgrim man and woman and the turkey, and if there's any time left, I'll give you *another* piece of paper and you can do your own picture with your own crayons. Can you do that?"

"I'll try," Tommy said, with a big smile.

And he did.

And he did.

And he still does.

TOMIE dePAOLA

Dear Houghton Mifflin Readers,

Did you know that when I was only four years old, I knew that I wanted to be an artist when I grew up? So, I decided to write the story about my wanting to be an artist.

It was fun telling all the things that really happened, but I made up some things, too. I made up some of the teachers' names. I made up that it happened in first grade. It really happened in second grade. But, I really did have sixty-four Crayola crayons. I really did have to draw a Pilgrim man, a Pilgrim woman, and a turkey! And I did draw pictures on my sheets!

When I grow up...

    When he was young, Tomie dePaola liked to draw pictures. When he grew up, he became an artist.

    What do YOU like to do? Make a list of four things you like to do now. Choose one thing on your list that you could do as a job when you grow up. Then draw a picture of yourself doing that job.

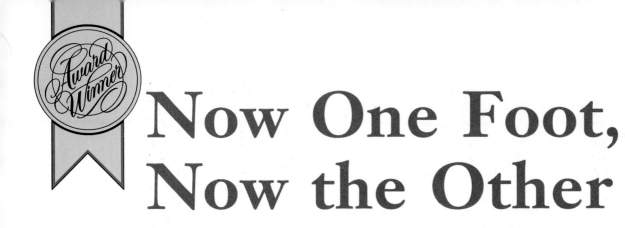

Now One Foot,
Now the Other

written and illustrated by Tomie dePaola

obby was named after his best friend, his grandfather, Bob. When Bobby was just a baby, his grandfather told everyone, "Bobby will be three years old before he can say Grandpa, so I'm going to have him call me Bob."

And "Bob" was the first word Bobby said.

Bob was the one who helped Bobby learn to walk.

"Hold on to my hands, Bobby," his grandfather said. "Now one foot, now the other."

One of the best things Bob and Bobby did was to play with the old wooden blocks that were kept on a shelf, in the small sewing room under the front stairs.

The blocks had letters on two sides, numbers on two sides and pictures of animals and other things on the last two sides. Bob and Bobby would slowly, very slowly put the blocks one on top of the other, building a tall tower. There were thirty blocks.

Sometimes the tower would fall down when only half the blocks were piled up.

Sometimes the tower would be almost finished.

"Just one more block," Bob would say.

"And that's the elephant block," Bobby would say.

And they would carefully put the elephant  block on the very top.

But Bob would sneeze and the tower would fall down. Bobby would laugh and laugh.

"Elephants always make you sneeze, Bob," Bobby would say.

"We'll just have to try the next time," his grandfather would say.

Then Bob would sit Bobby on his knee and tell him stories.

"Bob, tell me the story about how you taught me to walk," Bobby would say.

And his grandfather would tell Bobby how he held Bobby's hands and said, "Now one foot, now the other. And before you knew it . . ."

On Bobby's fifth birthday, Bob and he had a special day. They went to the amusement park. They rode a roller coaster, ate hot dogs and ice cream. They had their pictures taken in a machine, and they sang a song and made a phonograph record. And when it got dark, they watched the fireworks.

On the way home, Bob told Bobby stories.

"Now, tell me the story about how you taught me to walk," Bobby said.

And Bob did.

Not long after Bobby's birthday, his grandfather
got very sick. Bobby came home and his grandfather
wasn't there.

"Bob is in the hospital," Dad told Bobby. "He's had
what is called a *stroke*."

"I want to go see him," Bobby said.

"You can't, honey," Mom told him. "Right now
Bob's too sick to see anyone. He can't move his arms
and legs, and he can't talk. The doctor's not sure if he
knows who anyone is. We'll just have to wait and hope
Bob gets better."

Bobby didn't know what to do. He didn't want to eat; he had a hard time going to sleep at night. Bob just *had* to get better.

Months and months and months went by. Bob was still in the hospital. Bobby missed his grandfather.

One day when Bobby came home from school, his father told him that Bob was coming home.

"Now, Bobby," Dad said, "Bob is still very sick. He can't move or talk. When he sees your mother and me, he still doesn't know who we are, and the doctor doesn't think he'll get any better. So, don't be scared if he doesn't remember you."

But Bobby *was* scared. His grandfather *didn't* remember him. He just lay in bed. And when Dad carried him, Bob sat in a chair. But he didn't talk or even move.

One day, Bob tried to say something to Bobby, but the sound that came out was awful. Bobby ran out of the room.

"Bob sounded like a monster!" Bobby cried.

"He can't help it, Bobby," Mom said.

So, Bobby went back to the room where Bob was sitting. It looked like a tear was coming down Bob's face.

"I didn't mean to run away, Bob. I was scared. I'm sorry," Bobby said. "Do you know who I am?"

Bobby thought he saw Bob blink his eye.

"Mom, Mom," Bobby called. "Bob knows who I am."

"Oh, Bobby," Mom said. "You're just going to upset yourself. Your grandfather doesn't recognize any of us."

But Bobby knew better. He ran to the small sewing room, under the front stairs. He took the blocks off the shelf and ran back to where Bob was sitting.

Bob's mouth made a small smile.

Bobby began to build the tower.

Halfway . . .
Almost to the top . . .
Only one block left.

"OK, Bob," said Bobby. "Now the elephant block." And Bob made a strange noise that sounded like a sneeze.

The blocks fell down and Bob smiled and moved his fingers up and down.

Bobby laughed and laughed. Now he knew that Bob would get better.

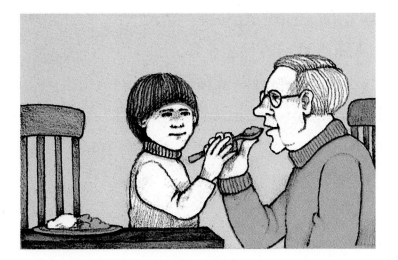

And Bob did. Slowly, he began to talk a little. It sounded strange but he could say "Bobby" just as clear as day. Bob began to move his fingers and then his hands. Bobby still helped to feed his grandfather, but one day Bob could almost hold a spoon by himself. But, he still couldn't walk.

When the weather got nice and warm, Dad carried Bob out to a chair set up on the lawn. Bobby sat with him.

"Bobby," Bob said. "Story." So, Bobby told Bob some stories.

Then, Bob stood up very slowly.

"You. Me. Walk," said Bob.

Bobby knew exactly what Bob wanted to do.

Bobby stood in front of Bob and let Bob lean on his shoulders.

"OK, Bob. Now one foot."

Bob moved one foot.

"Now the other foot."

Bob moved the other.

By the end of the summer, Bob and Bobby could walk to the end of the lawn and Bob could talk better and better each day.

On Bobby's sixth birthday, Bobby got the
blocks. Slowly he built up the tower. Only one
block to go.

"Here, elephant block," Bob said.

Bobby put it on top.

Bob sneezed!

"Elephants always
make you sneeze, Bob,"
Bobby said. "We'll just
have to try the next time.
Now, tell me some stories."

Bob did.

Then Bob said, "Bobby, tell story how you teach Bob to walk."

"Well, Bob, you leaned on my shoulders and then I said, 'Now one foot, now the other.' And before you knew it . . ."

TOMIE dePAOLA

The story you just read is based on something that really happened. My grandfather, Tom, had a stroke just like Bob in the story. I was a grown-up though, and my grandfather didn't get better. But the part about the blocks is real. If you came to visit me, you'd see them on a shelf in my living room.

Something Special

Bob and Bobby shared lots of special times
together. They built towers with blocks, told stories,
and spent a special day at the amusement park.

Think of a special time you have shared with
someone in your family. Tell a story about this time
to a classmate.

Strega Nona's Magic Lessons

STORY AND PICTURES BY

Tomie de Paola

ambolona, the baker's daughter, was angry. Every day, summer, fall, winter, and spring, she had to get up before the sun to bake the bread. Then, piling the loaves on her head, she went to deliver them. But her work wasn't finished. Rushing back to the bakery, she had to mix the flour and salt and water and yeast and set the dough to rise for tomorrow's bread.

"Don't forget," her father, the baker, would say, "to make the cookies and bake the cakes. And remember, Bambolona, to clean up everything spic and span! I'm going now to see my friends." And off he would go to sit all day in the square of the little town in Calabria.

One day Bambolona said, "Papa, there is too much work to do. I need some help."

"Get up earlier," her father said.

"But I get up now before the sun!" said Bambolona. "And I'm the last one in town to get to bed."

"That's the way things are," her father said as he went out the door on his way to the square. "And don't forget," he called back, "you have a wedding cake to bake."

That did it. Bambolona dusted the flour from her hands and took off her apron. "I'm going to *change* the way things are," she said. "I'll go see Strega Nona. She's so wise, she'll help me."

"I think I know how to help you," Strega Nona said after hearing Bambolona's sad tale. "So many people come to me with their troubles. I could certainly use some help. Why not stay with me and I will teach you my magic."

"Oh, Strega Nona," said Bambolona, "thank you!"

"We'll start today," said Strega Nona.

Now, Big Anthony, who worked around the house and in the garden for Strega Nona, was listening. He was always listening to what other people were talking about instead of working. "Strega Nona!" he shouted, running into the house. "Me too! Teach me your magic too!"

"Oh, Anthony," Strega Nona said with a smile, "I can't do that. Why don't you go and milk the goat." Now Big Anthony was the one who was angry!

"I'll show
Strega Nona,"
he muttered.
"I'll just go and
work for the
baker, now that

Bambolona has left." Down the hill Big Anthony ran.

The baker hired him on the spot. "The first thing
you do is mix the dough," the baker told Big Anthony.
"Put in this much flour, this much salt, this much
water, and this much yeast." He looked hard at Big
Anthony's smiling face.

"Do you understand? *The yeast makes the dough rise.* Now mix it right away, and by the time I get back at six o'clock, the dough will be ready to make into loaves."

"*Sì Signore* — yes sir!" Big Anthony said.

The baker walked out the door and toward the square.

"I'll just look at everything first," said Big Anthony, poking around.

"Cookies!" He ate one, then another. "Cakes!" He ate one, then another. Big Anthony ate them all. In fact, he was still eating when the clock in the square struck four.

"*Mamma mia!*" said Big Anthony. "I forgot to mix the dough. It won't rise in time. Ah! I know. *The yeast makes the dough rise!* I'll just put in a lot more of that, and the dough will rise much faster!"

"I'll still have time for a nap," he said when he got through. He sat down and promptly fell asleep.

What a sight the baker saw when he returned.

"OUT!" shouted the baker.

122

"What's the matter, Big Anthony?" asked Signora Rosa.

"The baker threw me out. Now I have no job," he answered. "And it's Strega Nona's fault. I never would have left her house if she had let me learn to be a *Strega*."

"Silly goose," said Signora Rosa. "Whoever heard of a man being a *Strega*?"

All of a sudden Big Anthony's eyes lit up, and off he ran.

"To cure a headache, you must first fill the bowl with water," Strega Nona was telling Bambolona. "Next you add a few drops of olive oil. Then you say these magic words . . ."

Knock, knock, knock. Strega Nona went to the door.

"Oh, Strega Nona," said a tall girl, standing there.
"All my life I've wanted to learn your magic. Will you
teach me? Please?"

"*Santo Cielo* — dear me," said Strega Nona. "What
is your name, my girl?"

"Uh-h-h — Antonia," said the girl.

"Why do you want to learn my magic, Antonia?"
Strega Nona asked.

"Oh, so that I can help people," said Antonia. "Ever
since I was a little girl, I've wanted to become a *Strega.*"

"Ah, in that case," said Strega Nona, "come right in.
This is Bambolona. She is learning my magic, too."

Bambolona stared at Antonia and then at Strega Nona.

"How nice. Two girls to teach," Strega Nona said. She smiled at Bambolona and then she began. "To learn magic and practice it well," she said, "you must learn to see *and* not to see. You must learn to remember *and* to forget; to be still *and* to be busy. But, mostly you must be faithful to your work. Do you understand, my dears?"

"*Sì* — yes, Strega Nona," said Bambolona.

"No — *no*," said Antonia. "When are we going to learn how to do the *magic* things?"

"In time," said Strega Nona. "Now let's practice some of the magic words. Repeat in the right order after me."

Soon Bambolona said all of them by heart. Antonia kept mixing them up.

Bambolona learned the cure for headaches.
Antonia didn't.

Bambolona learned to make love potions.
Antonia didn't.

Bambolona learned how to get rid of warts.
Antonia didn't.

"Bambolona," said Strega Nona, "I think you are ready now to learn more powerful magic. This is a special book. It is very ancient and contains many magic secrets. Tomorrow we will begin with it."

"Oh *Grazie,* Strega Nona," said Bambolona.

"Me too, Strega Nona?" asked Antonia.

"Not yet, Antonia," said Strega Nona. "You have other things to learn."

That night while everyone slept, Antonia crept into Strega Nona's house. "Bambolona thinks she's so smart," said Antonia. "I'll just read that book tonight, and tomorrow I'll surprise her *and* Strega Nona."

The next morning Antonia was looking very tired. "Antonia," said Strega Nona, "watch and listen. Come, Bambolona. We will start."

"Wait — wait," shouted Antonia. "I have a surprise. I know some *real* magic. Watch me turn that iron kettle into a golden one."

"Are you sure, Antonia?" said Strega Nona, frowning.

"Yes, oh yes," said Antonia, beginning to mutter some strange-sounding words. But she stopped. "Wait! I remember now." She began again.

"Be careful, Antonia," warned Bambolona. "Magic can't be fooled with."

"I've got it now," Antonia said.

She muttered more words. Suddenly there was a bright flash, some smelly smoke, and the iron kettle . . . was still *there*!

But Strega Nona wasn't. Instead, where Strega Nona had been standing was a nice fat TOAD.

"Now see what you've done!" cried Bambolona.

"Oh *no*!" shouted Antonia. "Oh help! Help, somebody! Save Strega Nona! What have I done?"

"Strega Nona warned you to be careful with magic.

Now she's gone forever," Bambolona said.

"Strega Nona," wept Antonia, picking up the toad, "forgive me, forgive me. Please, Bambolona, you're so clever, you're so smart, please change her back again! I promise I'll never play with magic again . . ."

"I can't change that toad into Strega Nona," said Bambolona. "But I *can* change Antonia into . . . Big Anthony!" Bambolona pulled off Antonia's kerchief and — sure enough — there was Big Anthony!

"Oh, I'll never learn," howled Big Anthony, "I'll never learn. Oh, Strega Nona — Strega Nona — what have I done to you?"

"Perhaps," said Bambolona, "if you really promise to never, ever play with magic again, that will bring Strega Nona back."

132

"Do you really think that would work?" said Big Anthony, sobbing.

"It's worth a try," said Bambolona.

Big Anthony put down the toad. He closed his eyes tight and put his hand over his heart. "I promise, I *really* promise, that as long as I live I will never play with magic again. Just please bring Strega Nona back."

There was another bright
flash, some smelly smoke, and
presto! Strega Nona was back!

"Where am I?" said Strega
Nona. "Oh, I'm in my little
house. Whatever happened to
me? Hello, Bambolona. And,
why, Big Anthony, what are *you*
doing here? Where's sweet Antonia?"

"Tell her, Big Anthony," said Bambolona.

"Oh, Strega Nona," said Big Anthony, falling on his knees. He told Strega Nona what he had done. He was so busy crying and talking, he didn't see the nice fat toad hopping past him out the door.

"And so, Strega Nona, please," he said, "if you take me back, I promise to be good. I'll do all my chores and never play with magic again."

"All right, Anthony," said Strega Nona, smiling. "But before you go back to work, change your clothes. You're wearing Signora Rosa's nicest dress."

TOMIE dePAOLA

<u>Strega Nona's Magic Lessons</u> is a made-up story. I'm so glad I thought up Strega Nona, Big Anthony, and Bambolona. Strega Nona is a little bit like my Italian grandmother, and Big Anthony is like one of my cousins. I guess I don't know anyone like Bambolona. I love these characters and I hope you do, too. There are now four books about Strega Nona and probably more to come.

Now What?

At the end of the story, Big Anthony promises Strega Nona that he'll NEVER play with magic again. But will he keep his promise?

Think about what might happen after Big Anthony makes his promise. Then, with a partner, play the roles of Big Anthony and Strega Nona. Act out what they might do and say next.

Here's a poem by Tomie dePaola.

He drew the picture too.

The Secret Place

It was my secret place —
    down at the foot
    of my bed —
    under the covers.

It was very white.

I went there
    with a book, a flashlight,
    and the special pencil
    that my grandfather gave me.

To read —
    and to draw pictures
    on all that white.

It was my secret place
    for about a week —

Until my mother came
    to change the sheets.

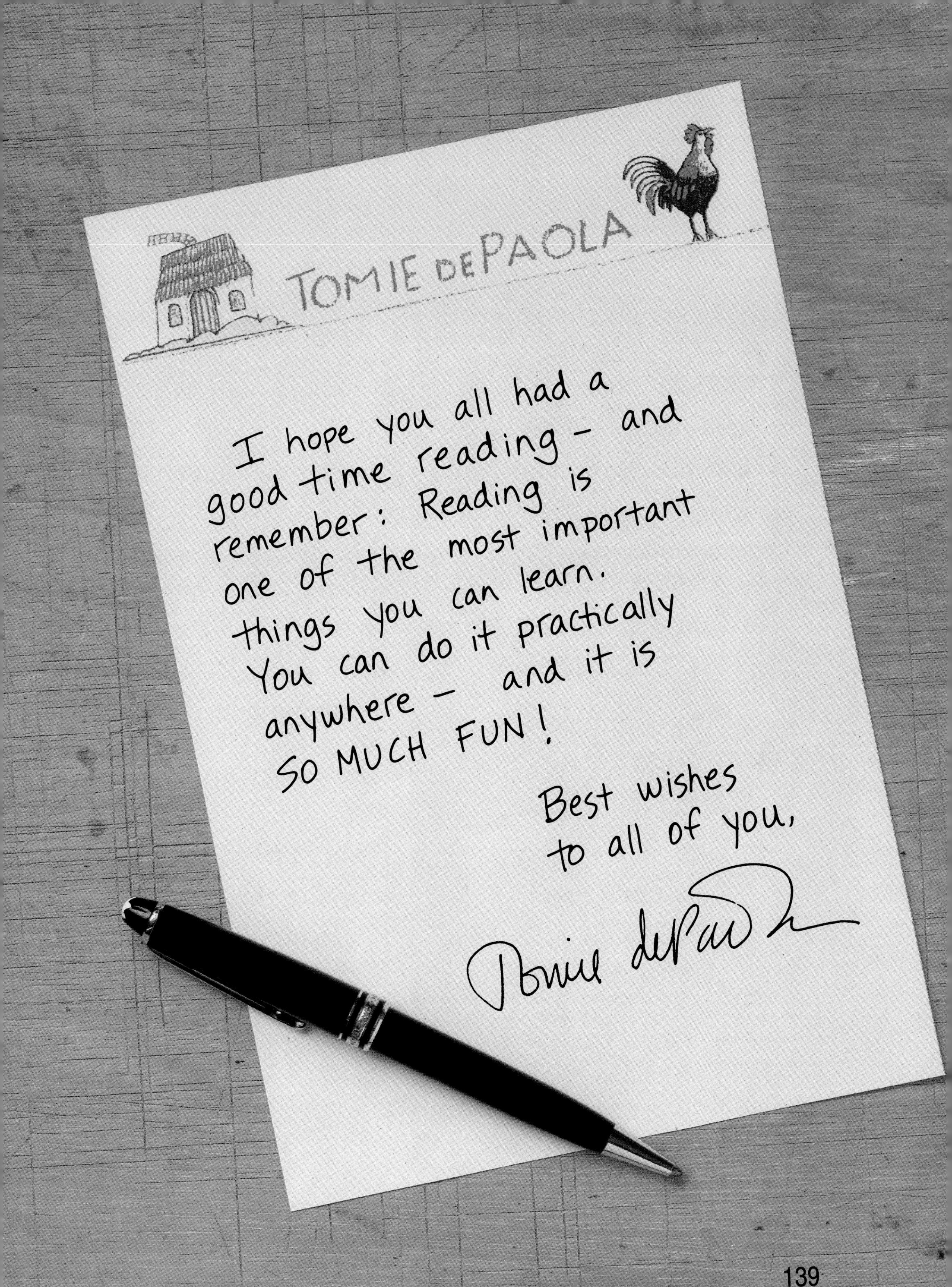

TOMIE dePAOLA

I hope you all had a good time reading — and remember: Reading is one of the most important things you can learn. You can do it practically anywhere — and it is SO MUCH FUN!

Best wishes
to all of you,

Tomie dePaola

Picture yourself reading these books

Like Tomie dePaola, other authors both write and illustrate their books. Here are two other Tomie dePaola books, plus books by three other authors who illustrate their own books.

The Quicksand Book
by Tomie dePaola

What is quicksand? Where is it found? This funny book will answer your questions about quicksand.

The Legend of the Bluebonnet
by Tomie dePaola

A girl gives up her favorite doll to help bring rain. The next morning she makes a surprising discovery.

THE LEGEND OF
THE BLUEBONNET

AN OLD TALE OF TEXAS
RETOLD AND ILLUSTRATED BY
TOMIE dePAOLA

*George and Martha
Round and Round*
by James Marshall

George and
Martha are two
hippos who are
friends forever in
these five funny
stories.

Stevie
by John Steptoe

Robert is unhappy
when Stevie comes to
stay at his house. Will Robert's
feelings about Stevie change?

Fox's Dream
by Tejima

A fox crosses a
magical winter
landscape and finds
his mate.

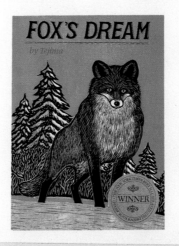

THEME 3

Aesop's Fables

Long, long ago a man named Aesop told stories called fables. Through these stories, Aesop tried to teach lessons, or morals, about how people should live.

People enjoyed Aesop's fables so much that they told them over and over again, in many different ways.

Now, from Aesop to you, here are some stories from long ago.

TABLE OF CONTENTS

146 **The Tortoise and the Hare**
retold and illustrated by Janet Stevens

164 **The Lion and the Mouse**
a play retold by Robert Hoffer
with illustrations by S. D. Schindler

180 **Pulín and Miga** *from* Pupurupú
retold by Sabine R. Ulibarrí
with illustrations by Darius Detwiler

The Tortoise
and the Hare

Janet Stevens

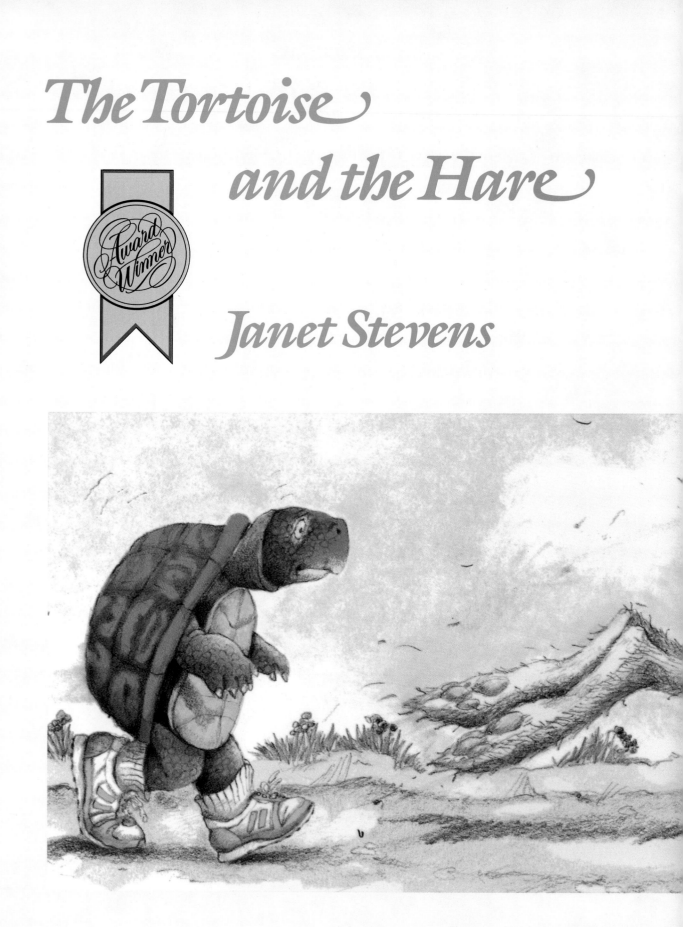

Once upon a time, there was a tortoise and a hare.

Tortoise was friendly and quiet. He did everything slowly. Hare was flashy and rude. He did everything quickly.

Hare liked to tease Tortoise about being so slow.

When Tortoise ate breakfast, Hare said, "By the time you finish your last bite, it will be dinnertime."

When Tortoise worked in his garden,
Hare said, "By the time you pick those spring
flowers, it will be winter."

One afternoon, Hare followed Tortoise to
the store. Hare teased him on the way. "By
the time you get there, the store will be
closed," he said. "You're so slow, I could
beat you at a race, hopping backwards on
one paw."

"But I could never beat you, Hare," said Tortoise.

"Yes, you could," said Tortoise's friends. "All you need is a little help."

"Then you *will* race me, Tortoise?" asked Hare.

Tortoise pulled his head into his shell.

"I don't want to," he said.

"You've got to," said his friends. "You've put up with that nasty hare long enough. We think you can win."

Tortoise didn't want to disappoint his friends, so he finally agreed to race against Hare.

Tortoise only had two-and-a-half weeks to get in shape before the big race. Rooster helped him out at the gym. Raccoon cooked him healthy meals. Frog went jogging with him every morning. By the day of the race, Tortoise was ready.

Animals from all over the county came to watch the tortoise and the hare.

Rooster read aloud the rules and described the course.

"Attention, everyone. The race will begin
when I sound this gong. The six-mile course
is marked by red flags. The first one to reach
the finish line wins. Runners, take your mark,
get set, GO!!" Raccoon sounded the gong.

Hare bolted out of sight before Tortoise
had taken his first step. The crowd roared
and cheered as Tortoise inched forward.

Hare was so far ahead that he decided to stop at Bear's house for something cool to drink.

Hare rested and sipped lemonade. Bear noticed something moving outside the window. "Hare, there goes Tortoise."

"What?" yelled Hare, running out the door.

Hare passed Tortoise for the second time. Then he decided to stop at Mouse's house for a snack.

As Hare munched on crackers and cheese, Mouse yelled, "Is that Tortoise I see out the window?"

"I'm not worried about that slowpoke," said Hare. "I've passed him twice already." Then he finished his snack and hopped out the door.

Hare passed Tortoise for a third time. Now, he was far ahead. He saw a pond and decided to stop and rest. The snacks had made him sleepy.

Hare was so sure that he would win, he took a nap in the soft grass. As he closed his eyes, he dreamed of victory.

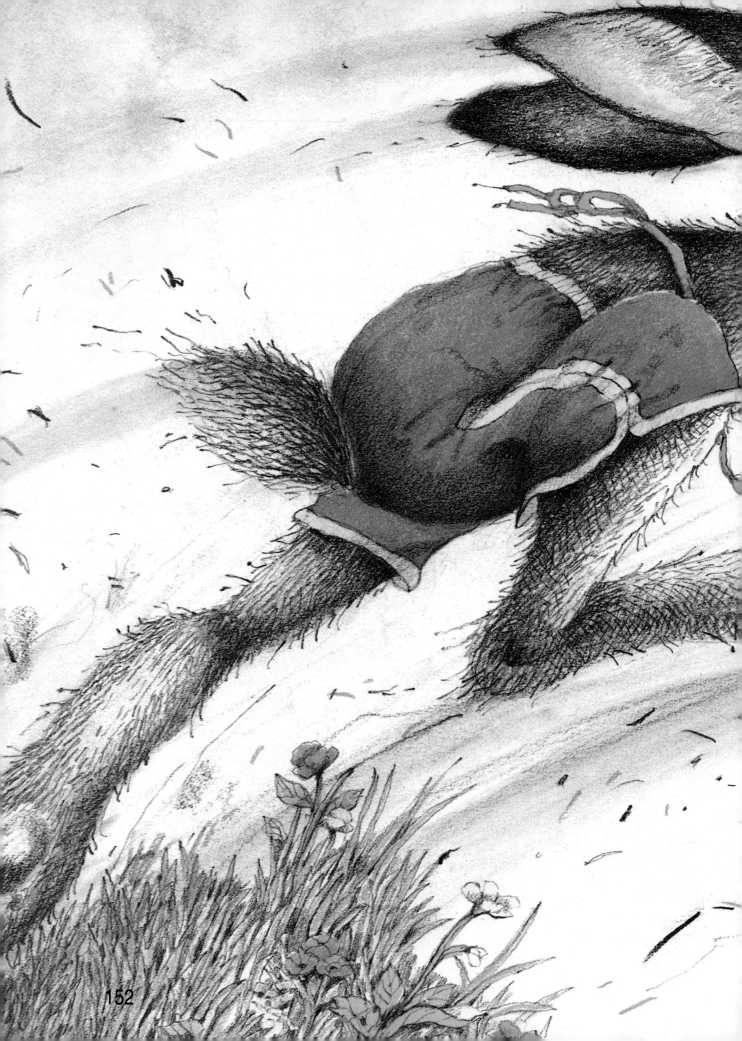

Suddenly, Hare woke up because the crowd was cheering.

"Yay, Tortoise," the crowd roared.

Tortoise was two steps away from the finish line.

"Slow down, you bowlegged reptile," screamed Hare as he tried to catch up.

But it was too late. Tortoise crossed the line just before the tornado of dust and fur that was Hare flew by. Tortoise had won the race. Hare couldn't believe it. That measly shell on legs had beaten him.

Tortoise smiled as his friends carried him on their shoulders. He had learned an important lesson:

HARD WORK AND PERSEVERANCE BRING REWARD.

TORTOISE

On Your Mark . . .

With a partner, make a map of the racecourse. Draw it on a piece of cardboard or paper. Show the places where Hare stopped. Then make cardboard figures of Tortoise and Hare. Use them to act out the story for your class.

VS HARE

About the Author and Illustrator

When **Janet Stevens** met Tomie dePaola in 1978, he encouraged her to turn a popular children's song into a book. So she created *Animal Fair,* which was her first picture book.

Since then, Janet Stevens has illustrated over ten books. She has retold and illustrated stories by Aesop and Mother Goose. You may enjoy reading her retelling of *Androcles and the Lion.*

The Tortoise and the Hare

retold in verse by Tom Paxton
illustrated by Robert Rayevsky

"Zip! Zap! Zoom! Look at me go!
I am the hare, and I hope you know
A streak of lightning could not catch me;
I am as fast as fast can be."

"Fast, indeed," the tortoise replied,
"And yet, I wonder, if I tried
To win a race, how well I'd do.
I think I'd like to race with you."

"To race with me is lunacy!
Just search through all of history;
No greater mismatch you'll find there
Than a tortoise racing against a hare."

But the tortoise insisted on racing, and so
The starter cried, "Get ready! Go!"
Then Whiz! Bang! Boom! In a streak of light,
The hare was quickly out of sight.

Zip! Zoom! and Whiz! and Wham! and Screech!
"I guess this race is out of reach,"
The hare exclaimed as he stopped by a tree.
"That tortoise will never catch up with *me*."

He stretched out under the sunny skies,
And very soon had closed his eyes.
He slept and dreamt of carrot pie,
While the tortoise slowly plodded by.

The hare awoke and washed his face,
Then quickly finished up the race,
When — what a shock for Mister Hare! —
He found the tortoise waiting there!

To cheers that rang across the skies,
The tortoise took the winner's prize.
Yes, many there are who race and run,
But slow and steady gets things done.

The Lion and the Mouse

a play retold by Robert Hoffer
illustrated by S. D. Schindler

Characters: Lion

Mouse

Hunter 1

Hunter 2

Hunter 3

Hunter 4

Hunter 5

Scene 1

(The setting is a clearing in a forest. Lion enters the clearing and sits down.)

Lion: GRR-ROWF! Am I tired! *(He gives his mane a shake.)* It's not easy being the King of Beasts! Roaring all day, roaring all night. Making sure those little animals know who's boss . . . *(He yawns.)* I think it's time to take a little nap. (Lion *lies down and begins to snore.)*
(Mouse *enters from the left.)*

Mouse: Chew and nibble, nibble and chew . . . mousing around is fun to do . . .

(Mouse *sees* Lion *and stops.*)

Mouse: Oh no! It's the Lion! I'd better get out of here! *(Pause)* Wait a second. He's asleep.

(Mouse *goes a little nearer.*)

Mouse: Wow. This is the closest I've ever come to the King of Beasts. I wonder if I can go even closer. *(He sings softly:)* Rock-a-bye Lion, in the treetop . . . Look at this! I'm standing on his tail! And now I'm standing on his paw! And now —

Lion: Aha! I've got you!

Mouse: Oh, no! I've been caught by the lion — my worst nightmare!

Lion: Oh boy! I've captured a mouse — my favorite snack!

Mouse: Wait! Stop! Please, don't eat me!

Lion: Why shouldn't I eat you? You woke me up, didn't you?

Mouse: Yes, I did, and I'm very sorry.

Lion: You stood on my paw, didn't you?

Mouse: I'll never do it again, I promise.

Lion: I know you won't do it again, because I'm going to eat you right now.

Mouse: No, wait. Don't do that. Listen — if you let me go, I'll . . . I'll . . .

Lion: Yes? What will you do?

Mouse: I'll be your friend for life.

Lion *(Chuckling)*: My friend for life! Oh, what an honor!

Mouse: I'm serious! A mouse can be a very valuable friend to have! Maybe I can help you sometime.

Lion *(Laughing)*: *You* help *me?* Oh, that's a good one. That's the best joke I've heard all week! A teensy little mouse helping the King of Beasts! *(Lion laughs some more.)* Mouse, do you know something? You've put me in such a good mood with your joke, I'm going to let you go.

168

Mouse: That is a wise decision! You won't be sorry!
Remember, anytime you need me, just give a roar!
(Mouse scurries off.)

Lion: Oh, I will, don't worry. *(To himself)* A mouse
helping a lion. What a ridiculous idea!
*(Lion curls up and goes back to sleep, still
chuckling.)*

Scene 2

(The setting is another part of the forest, a few days later.)

Hunter 1: Shh . . . I think I hear him coming.

Hunter 2: Who?

Hunter 3: The lion!

Hunter 4: Are we catching a lion? Oops — I just remembered something I forgot to do at home.

Hunter 5: Come back here and be quiet . . .

(Lion *enters from the right.*)

Lion: All right, make way, make way. Here comes the King of Beasts. Give me some room.

(Hunters *come rushing out and throw a net over* Lion.*)

Lion: Hey, what's going on? Get this thing off me!

Hunter 1: We've got him! We've got him!

Hunter 3: Quick, tie him down!

Hunter 4: You tie him down. I'll keep an eye out for tigers.

Hunter 5: Come on! Get busy and hammer down these ropes.

Hunter 2: Watch out for his claws!

Hunter 1: There! That does it. Now, let's go find a cage.

Hunter 4: I have a birdcage.

Hunter 5: Not a birdcage. A lion cage!

Hunter 2: Shouldn't one of us stay here and guard him?

Hunter 3: Don't be silly. He can't escape from those ropes.

(Hunters *exit.*)

Lion: Help! This is terrible! Me — the King of Beasts — caught like a mouse in a trap! Oh, the shame of it all! The humiliation! *(Lion roars.)* *(Mouse enters from the left.)*

Mouse: Did you roar, Lion?

Lion: Oh, it's you, is it? All right, go ahead, Mouse. Have your laugh. The mighty King doesn't look so mighty now, does he? *(Lion starts to cry.)* Oh, woe and misery! It's the zoo for me! They'll lock me up and throw away the key! *(Mouse walks around Lion, rubbing his chin, nodding to himself.)*

Mouse: Hmm, let me see. Yes, these shouldn't be any problem. I'll just start with this one . . .

Lion: *(He stops crying.)* What are you doing, Mouse?

Mouse: Chew and nibble, nibble and chew . . . gnawing on ropes is fun to do . . .

Lion: You're chewing through the ropes!

Mouse: That's one . . .

Lion: Mouse! Wonderful!

Mouse: That's two . . .

Lion: Hurry! They'll soon be back with a cage!

Mouse: And that's the last one.

Lion: I'm free! Mouse! You did it!

Mouse: Just in time, too. Here they come.

Lion: Quick, let's hide behind this bush!

(Hunters *enter from the left.*)

Hunter 1: Okay, Mr. Lion. Here's your new — Hey!

Hunter 2: He's gone!

Hunter 3: It looks as if he gnawed through the ropes.

Hunter 4: I didn't know lions gnawed.

Hunter 5: This is all your fault! I told you we should have guarded him!

Hunter 1 (*Pointing at* Hunter 2): It was those knots you made!

Hunter 2: My knots were fine!

Hunter 3: They were not!

Hunter 5: Yours were so loose a mouse could have escaped from them!

(Lion *steps out from behind bushes.*)

Hunter 4: Um . . . fellows. I think we have company.

Lion: ROARRR!

Hunters: Let's get out of here!

(Hunters *exit in a hurry.*)

Lion (*Yelling after them*): And don't come back!

Mouse: — or else!

Lion (*Turning to* Mouse): Mouse, you really came
through for me. (Lion *puts out his paw.*)
Thanks, pal.

Mouse (*Shaking* Lion's *paw*): Didn't I tell you that a
    mouse can be a valuable friend to have?

Lion: You sure did. Today I learned that a small
    friend can be a great friend. (Lion *snaps his
    fingers.*) Hey, I just remembered! I have two
    pieces of cheesecake in the refrigerator. Will you
    join me, Mouse?

Mouse: I'd be delighted, Lion.

    (*They put their arms around each other and exit to
    the right.*)

A Tale of Two Friends

Did it seem strange to you that a lion and a mouse became friends? Think of another pair of animals that would make strange friends — a cat and a bird? a pig and a giraffe? Make up a story about how the two animals become friends. Tell how one helps the other.

About the Author

Robert Hoffer has written several plays for children about animals with funny or interesting problems. They include *The Groundhog's Shadow, Rudolf the Red-Nosed Genius,* and *Rabbit, Rabbit.*

About the Illustrator

S. D. Schindler has illustrated other traditional stories, including *Favorite Nursery Tales,* retold by Morrell Gipson, and *The Golden Goose and Other Tales of Good Fortune.*

from *Pupurupú*
retold by **Sabine R. Ulibarrí**
illustrated by **Darius Detwiler**

Pulín and Miga

It was the end of summer. The leaves were falling, the wind was singing its autumn song, and winter was knocking at the door.

Along the tiny hidden roads in the field, the ants were on the march. All day, every day, they worked. They had to store food before the snow fell. They had to get ready for the long, cold months ahead.

The busiest, hardest-working ant of all was Miga. Up and down the bumps in the road she went, a heavy load on her back. A grain of wheat weighed a ton. A kernel of corn weighed two tons. But how good the food would taste in the middle of winter — especially the piñón nuts!

So, Miga did her part to fill up the food bins, grain by grain, piñón nut by piñón nut. Even though she was tired, and sometimes stumbled under her load, she never rested.

In her travels Miga would often see Pulín the grasshopper sitting in the shade of a tree. He never worked. He was always munching leaves and sipping milkweed.

Miga couldn't help liking Pulín. He was the picture of elegance in his dark glasses, straw hat, and sport suit. All day long he strummed his guitar and sang songs. Miga liked to listen to Pulín's songs. They made the load she was carrying feel lighter. This one was Pulín's favorite:

I sing my song
to the sky.
I sing my song
to the wind.
Cica, cica, cica!

I sing my song
to the tree.
I sing my song
to the flower.
Cica, cica, cica!

I sing my song
to the leaves.
I sing my song
to the roses.
Cica, cica, cica!

One day Pulín stopped Miga on her way.

"Good morning, *amiga* Miga," he said, strumming his guitar.

"Good morning, friend Pulín."

"Come and sing a song with me, won't you?"

"I can't, Pulín. Winter is coming. I have to work. Besides, I don't know how to sing."

"Then I'll teach you!"

"I don't have time, Pulín. I'm sorry."

Miga went on with her load. Pulín shrugged and went on singing.

In this way, autumn went by. Winter came, and with it the cold. The first snow fell.

The ants disappeared from the field. Pulín stopped singing his songs. The whole world was white, still, and silent.

Meanwhile, Miga and the other ants were happy in their underground home. The ants kept on working. Some cooked, some cleaned house, others washed and ironed.

In the middle of all this activity there came a
weak knock at the door. Miga hurried to see who it
was. There in a gust of wind and snow stood Pulín.
His suit was dirty and torn. His feet were wrapped
in rags. In a voice shaking with cold, he whispered,
"Miga . . . *amiga mía* . . ."

"Pulín, my friend!" cried Miga. "What has happened to you?"

"I'm hungry . . . freezing . . . sick . . ."

"You should be home in bed!"

"I have no home . . . no family. You are the only friend I have."

"Come in, Pulín! Come in!"

Slowly the grasshopper dragged his frozen feet inside.

He was amazed by what he saw. There was a cozy fire in the fireplace. There were lovely pictures on the walls. Best of all, there were delicious smells coming from the kitchen.

The ants hurried to take care of Pulín. They served him a hot stew, gave him warm clothes, and bandaged his feet. Then they tucked him into bed in his own room.

With such friendly care Pulín soon became his old cheerful self. He began to teach the ants to sing. Before long they were all singing "Cica, cica, cica," while Pulín played the piano.

Meanwhile, the ants also had something to teach Pulín: how to work. Every day he learned a new task. He was surprised. Work wasn't that bad. He liked it!

When spring came, Pulín and his friends the ants went out in the fields again. But now everything had changed.

Pulín stopped spending every day lazing around under a tree. He started a school for young grasshoppers. He taught them how to build houses and store food for the winter.

The ants began to sing and tell jokes as they worked. It made their work feel much easier.

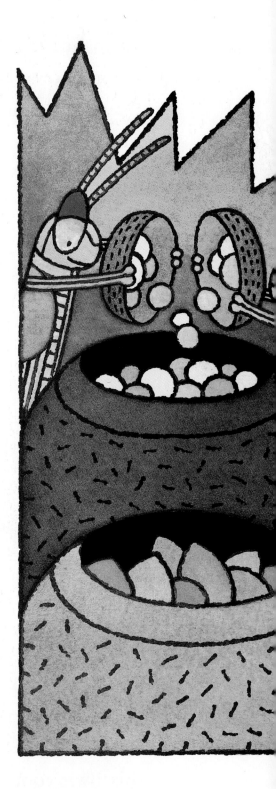

189

All the other animals were amazed.
Grasshoppers sweeping their front porches?
Thousands of ants singing "Cica, cica, cica"? Who
would have believed it?

But thanks to the friendship between Miga and
Pulín, life became better for both grasshoppers and
ants. So it is with all creatures: we have much to
teach each other and much to learn from each other.

Come One, Come All!

Pulin has started a school for grasshoppers who want to learn to work. But he needs an advertisement to let all the grasshoppers know about it. Meet with a friend. Draw and write an advertisement for Pulin's school. Tell what the grasshoppers will learn and why they should come.

About the Author

Sabine R. Ulibarrí was born and still lives in the state of New Mexico. He has been a teacher for over fifty years. Besides writing stories in English and Spanish, he has written poetry, essays, and books that teach the Spanish language.

"Pulín and Miga" is from Sabine R. Ulibarrí's book of stories for children, *Pupurupú*. The book includes such stories as the adventures of a roadrunner and a coyote, a pony from outer space, and a duck who learns to fly south for the winter.

About the Illustrator

Darius Detwiler grew up in Venezuela, in South America. In his drawings, he uses the bright colors of the Venezuelan hills. He has illustrated several picture books, including *El Dinosaurio se Cayo, Everyone Has a Job to Do,* and *Colors.* He now lives in San Antonio, Texas, where his cartoons often appear in the local newspaper.

Many countries around the world have fables of their own. Here is one more book of Aesop's fables and other fables from the United States, China, and the African nation of Zaire.

Once in a Wood: Ten Tales from Aesop

by Eve Rice

Read some of your favorite fables again and some new ones in this book of fables.

The Empty Pot

by Demi

To choose his successor, the Emperor of China gives each child a flower seed to grow. Why is Ping's flowerpot the only one that is empty?

Fables Near and Far

Fables

by Arnold Lobel

Here are twenty original fables about pigs, ostriches, kangaroos, and other animals who learn important lessons.

Traveling to Tondo

by Verna Aardema

Bowane the civet cat is traveling to Tondo to get married, but his three friends make him late for his wedding — *very* late.

THEME 4

IN and OUT of TROUBLE

There's nothing but trouble for the characters in this book. Nessa must keep a fox, some wolves, and a bear away from the fish she's caught. Curious George gets caught in a room full of soapsuds. Tye May gets into trouble when she won't help a greedy emperor. All of this certainly spells T – R – O – U – B – L – E. You'll read how the characters in this book get into trouble and how they get out of it.

CONTENTS

Nessa's Fish   200

by Nancy Luenn

with illustrations by Neil Waldman

Curious George Gets a Medal   226

written and illustrated by H. A. Rey

Tye May and the Magic Brush   246

written and illustrated by

Molly Garrett Bang

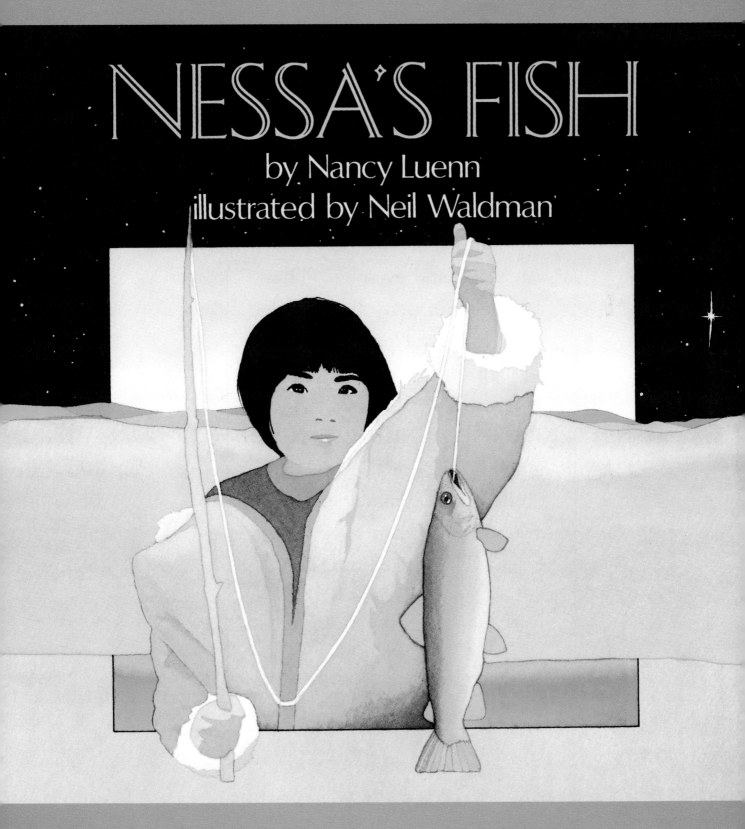

NESSA'S FISH

by Nancy Luenn
illustrated by Neil Waldman

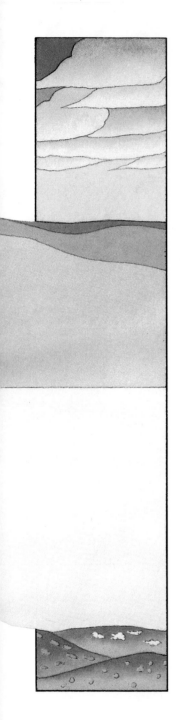

At autumn camp, Nessa and her grandmother walked inland half a day to fish in the stony lake.

They jigged for fish all afternoon and evening. They caught more than they could carry home. They caught enough to feed everyone in camp.

Nessa and her grandmother stacked up the fish. They piled stones over them to keep away the foxes. Then, tired out, they fell asleep.

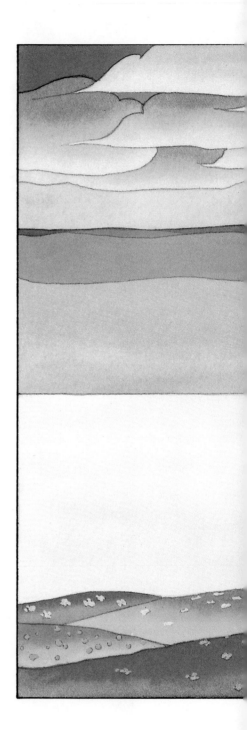

During the night, her grandmother was very sick from something she had eaten. Morning came and she needed to rest until she felt better.

Nessa watched over her grandmother. She brought her fresh water from the stony lake. She sat beside her while the sun rose slowly in the sky.

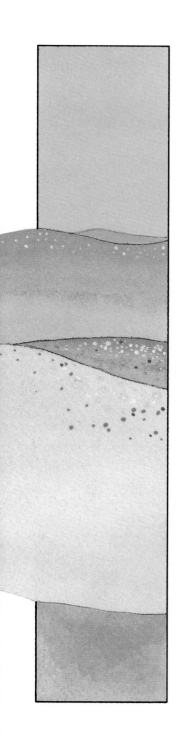

At noon a fox came and sniffed at the stones that covered the fish.

"Go away."

Her grandmother's voice was only a whisper. The fox didn't listen.

Nessa flapped her arms and shouted, "Go away!"

The fox dashed off across the tundra.

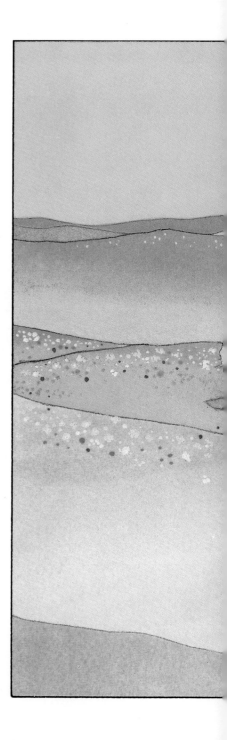

The sun rolled a little lower in the sky. A pack of wolves loped toward them and grinned at the stones that covered the fish.

"Do wolves eat fish?" asked Nessa, but her grandmother was asleep. Nessa thought she knew what to do. Her grandfather had taught her how to talk to wolves.

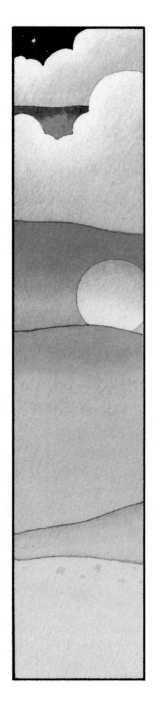

She made herself as tall as she could. She made her hands into ears, tipped them forward, and stared straight into the lead wolf's yellow eyes.

"Go away," she growled. "These are *our* fish."

The wolf lowered his tail and grinned apologies at Nessa. He led his pack away across the tundra.

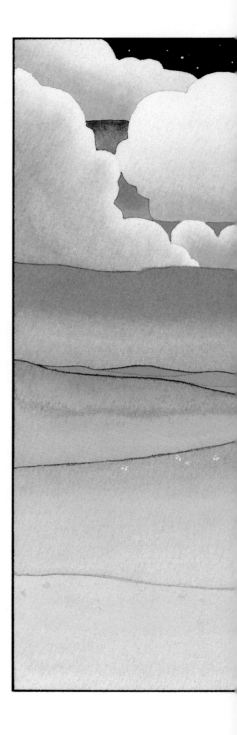

The sun sank behind
the hills. Shadows reached
across the land. Out of the
shadows came a huge, brown
bear. Nessa shivered. Bears
ate almost *anything*. She
wanted to run, but her
mother had told her never to
run from bears. She waved
her fishing pole at the bear
and shouted, "Go away!"

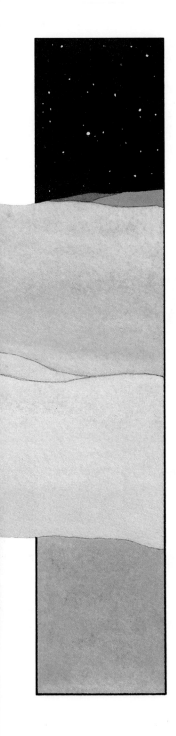

The bear stood up on its hind legs and stared. Nessa looked at its long, sharp claws. Would it eat all the fish? Would it eat her grandmother? Would it eat her, too? She tried to remember how to talk to bears.

Her father had told her that a bear would go away if you made it feel foolish. Nessa began to sing.

Skinny old bear
Fur falling out
Big ugly paws
And long pointy snout!

The bear looked
surprised. It took one step
backward, then another.
Nessa sang again.

Skinny old bear
Foolish thing
You can't sing
You can't sing!

The bear's long face did
look foolish. It *couldn't* sing.
It turned around and shuffled
off across the tundra.

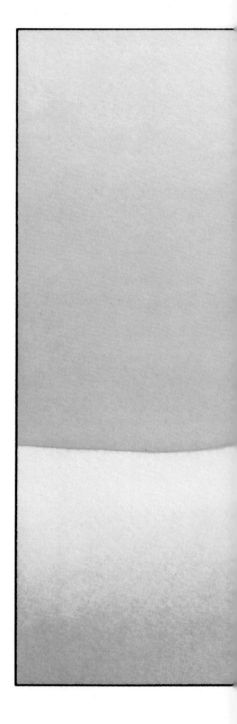

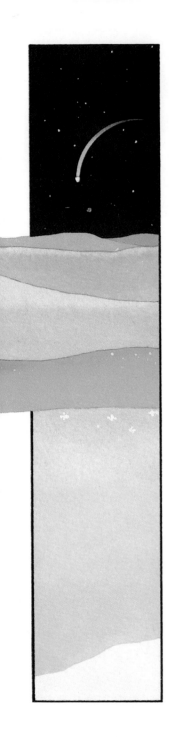

Nessa was very tired.
Her grandmother was sleeping.
She tried to stay awake, for
she had to watch over her.

But no one had told her
how to make sleep go away.

The moon rose over the
tundra. It shone down on
Nessa, fast asleep, curled up
beside her grandmother.
It shone on the stones that
covered the fish.

The moon watched over
them all until a noise woke
Nessa.

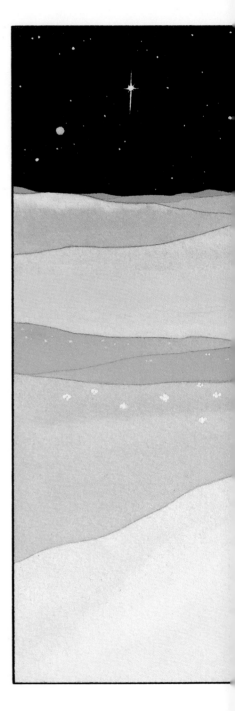

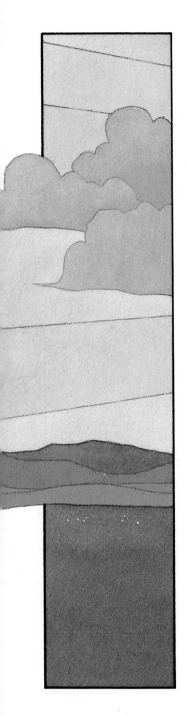

She grabbed her fishing
pole and sat up very tall. Was
it the fox? Was it the wolves?
Was it the *bear*?

It was her grandfather!
With him were her mother
and father and all of the dogs.
They had come to look for
Nessa and her grandmother.

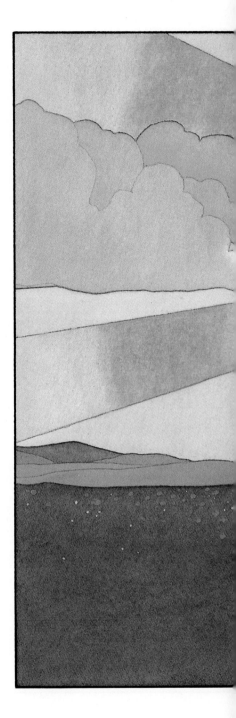

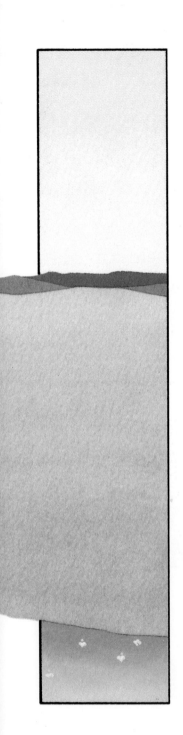

Everyone hugged her. The dogs waved their tails. Her grandmother woke up and smiled.

Nessa felt good. She had watched over her grandmother. And she had guarded the fish that would feed everyone in camp.

When morning came again, her grandmother felt better. They put the fish in skin bags for the dogs to carry. Then they all walked homeward half a day to autumn camp.

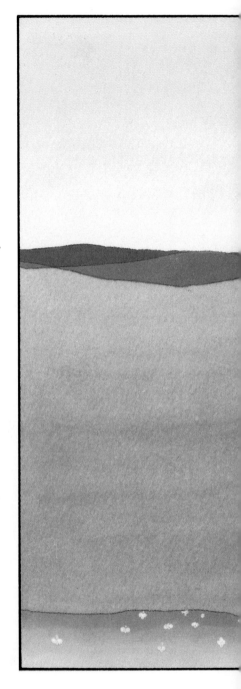

With a partner, make some puppets and act out Nessa's story. Draw pictures of Nessa, her grandmother, the fox, the wolf, the bear, and Nessa's mother, father, and grandfather. Cut out the characters and paste each one on a craft stick. Then one of you can read from the story while the other uses the puppets to show the action.

PUPPET
THEATRE
PRESENTS

About the Author and the Illustrator

Nancy Luenn

Nancy Luenn grew up in a house full of unusual pets, including guinea pigs, ducks, and a king snake. Nancy Luenn's love for animals and nature has

given her many ideas for stories. You may enjoy reading her book *The Dragon Kite.*

Neil Waldman

Neil Waldman has been an illustrator for many years — and not only of books. He has designed postage stamps for ten different countries.

Curious George
gets a medal
by
H. A. REY

This is George.

He lived with his friend, the man with the yellow
hat. He was a good little monkey — but he was always
curious.

George was alone this morning, looking at a
picture book, when the doorbell rang.

It was the mailman.

"Here is a letter for you," he said. "Put it on your
friend's desk. He'll read it to you when he comes
home."

George was curious. It was not often that
somebody wrote him. Too bad he could not read
the letter — but maybe he could write one himself!
In the top drawer of the desk there was paper and ink
and a fountain pen.

George sat down on the floor
and began to write — but the pen
was dry. It needed ink; George
would have to fill it. He
got a funnel from the
kitchen and started
pouring ink . . .

But instead of going
into the pen the ink spilled all over and made
a big blue puddle on the floor. It was an awful mess.

Quickly George got the blotter from the desk, but
that was no help; the puddle grew bigger all the time.
George had to think of something else.

Why, soap and water — that's what you clean up
with! From the kitchen shelf he got a big box of soap
powder and poured all the powder over the ink. Then
he pulled the garden hose through the window, opened
the tap, and sprayed water on the powder.

Bubbles began to form, and then some lather, and more lather and more lather AND MORE LATHER. In no time the whole room was full of lather — so full, indeed, that George had to escape in a hurry . . .

When he was safely out of the house, he first turned off the tap. But what next? How could he get rid of all the lather before his friend came home?

George sat down in the grass and thought for a long time. Finally he had an idea: he would get the big shovel and shovel the lather out of the window!

But where WAS the lather? While George had been outside thinking, it had all turned into water. Now the room looked like a lake and the furniture like islands in it.

The shovel was no use. A pump was what George needed to get the water out, and he knew just where to find one: he had seen a portable pump at the farm down the road.

The farmer was away working in the fields. Nobody noticed George when he got the pump out of the shed.

It was heavy. He would need help to pull it all the way back to the house.

Maybe he could tie the goat to the pump and make her pull it? But just as George was about to slip the loop over the goat's head — he was hurled through the air and landed near a pen full of pigs.

The biggest pig was standing near the gate. What if George opened the gate just enough to let him out? A big pig could easily pull a small pump.

Carefully, George lifted the latch — and before he knew it, ALL the pigs had burst out of the pen, grunting and squealing and trying to get away as fast as they could. George was delighted. He had never seen anything like it. For the moment all his troubles were forgotten . . .

But now the pigs were all gone, and not a single one was left to help him with the pump.

Luckily, there were cows grazing nearby. Cows were gentle and strong. It would mean nothing to a cow to pull the pump for him.

This time George was right; the cow did not mind being tied to the pump. She even let him climb on her back — and off they went! George was glad. Now he would soon be home, pump out the room, and everything would be all right.

Meanwhile the farmer and his son had heard the squealing of the pigs. They rushed home from the fields and now had their hands full catching all the pigs. Not until the last pig was safely back in the pen did they have time to look around. And what did they see? A little monkey riding on their cow, making off with their pump!

The chase was on! George and the cow were ahead at first. But the pump was slowing them down. The farmers were getting closer and closer. Now they had almost caught up with them — but WHERE WAS GEORGE?

Here he was — hiding in a shirt! The farmers had run past him. But on their way home they had to come back over the same road. George did not feel safe in his hiding place . . . Just then a truck came rattling down the road.

George jumped aboard (monkeys are good at jumping) and was gone before the farmers had a chance to see him.

The truck drove to a part of town that George had never seen before. At last it stopped in front of a large building. It was the Museum. George did not know what a museum was. He was curious. While the guard was busy reading his paper, George slipped inside.

He walked up the steps and into a room full of all sorts of animals. At first George was scared, but then he noticed that they did not move. They were not alive. They were stuffed animals, put into the Museum so that everybody could get a good look at them.

DINOSAUR (EXTINCT)

In the next room George saw something so
enormous it took his breath away. It was a dinosaur.
George was not scared this time; he knew it was not
real. He looked at the dinosaur and then at the baby
dinosaur — and then he saw the palm tree full of nuts.
George liked nuts. Suddenly he felt very hungry (he
had missed lunch that day). He would climb up and . . .

Do not touch!

BABY DINOSAUR

Just then he heard footsteps. He had to hide again —
but where?

A family came in to take a look at the dinosaur.
They paid no attention to the little monkey who was
standing there. The monkey did not move. He stood
so still they thought he was just another stuffed
animal . . .

George was glad when they were gone! Now he could pick the nuts. He climbed up the dinosaur's neck and started to pull, but the nuts would not come off (George did not know they were not real either). He pulled harder and harder, the tree began to sway . . .

CRASH! Down came the tree on the dinosaur's head, down came the dinosaur, and down came George!

Guards came rushing in from all sides, and underneath the fallen dinosaur they found a little monkey! They pulled him out of there and brought him to Professor Wiseman, who was the director of the Museum. Professor Wiseman was terribly angry. "Lock that naughty monkey up right away," he said, "and take him back to the zoo. He must have run away from there."

George was carried off in a cage. He felt so ashamed he almost wished he were dead . . . Suddenly the door opened. "George!" somebody shouted. It was his friend, the man with the yellow hat! "It seems you got yourself into a lot of trouble today," he said. "But maybe this letter here will get you out of it. It's from Professor Wiseman; he needs your help for an experiment. I found it on my desk at home; but I couldn't find YOU anywhere, so I came over here to talk to the Professor."

And this is what the letter said:

MUSEUM OF SCIENCE

Dear George,

A small space ship has been built by our experimental station. It is too small for a man but could carry a little monkey. Would you be willing to go up in it?

I have never met you but I hear that you are a bright little monkey who can do all sorts of things, and that is just what we need.

We want you to do something nobody has ever done before: bail out of a space ship in flight.

When we flash you a signal you will have to open the door and bail out with the help of emergency rockets.

We hope that you are willing and that your friend will permit you to go.

Gratefully Yours
Professor Wiseman
Director of the Science Museum.

"So YOU are George!" Professor Wiseman said.
"If I had only known . . . Of course everything will be
forgiven, if you are willing to go."

They got the smallest size space suit for George
and all the other things he needed for the flight. Then
they helped him put them on and showed him how to
use them. When everything was ready, a truck drove
up with a special television screen mounted on it to
watch the flight. They all got on and were off to the
launching site. They checked all the controls of the
space ship, especially the lever that opened the door.
George tried it, too.

The great moment had come. George waved good-by and went aboard. The door was closed. Professor Wiseman began to count: "Five — four — three — two — one — GO!"

He pressed the button and the ship rose into the air, slowly first, and then faster and faster and higher and higher, until they could no longer see it in the sky. But on the screen they saw George clearly all the time.

Now the moment had come for George to bail out. Professor Wiseman flashed the signal. They watched the screen: George did not move. Why didn't he pull the lever? In a few seconds it would be too late. The ship would be lost in outer space, with George in it!

They waited anxiously . . . At last George began to move.

Slowly, as if in a daze, he was groping for the lever. Would he reach it in time? There — he had grabbed it! The door opened — hurrah — George was on his way!

Out of the blue an open parachute came floating down to earth. The truck raced over to the spot where George would land.

What a welcome for George!

Professor Wiseman hung a big golden medal around his neck. "Because," he said, "you are the first living being to come back to earth from a space flight." And on the medal it said: To George, the First Space Monkey.

Then a newspaperman took his picture and everybody shouted and cheered, even the farmer and his son, and the kind woman from next door (who had worked for hours to get the water out of the room).

"I'm proud of you, George," said the man with the yellow hat. "I guess the whole world is proud of you today."

It was the happiest day in George's life.

SPEECH, SPEECH!

The crowd roared when Professor
Wiseman gave Curious George his medal.
Think about the things Curious George did
to earn the medal. Next, decide what Professor
Wiseman might have said to him when he
gave George the medal. Write down
a few ideas first. Then say your
speech to a group of your
classmates.

TO GEORGE
THE FIRST
1
SPACE MONKEY

About the Author and Illustrator

H. A. Rey

H. A. Rey spent most of his free time as a child drawing the animals at a nearby zoo. When he grew up, he wrote many books about a friendly monkey called Curious George.

You can follow more of George's adventures in the following books:

Curious George Takes a Job Imagine Curious George as a window washer or a painter. As usual, his curiosity gets him into trouble.

Curious George Rides a Bike The man with the yellow hat has given George a new bike. George promised he would stay close to home, but . . .

Cecily G. and the Nine Monkeys Cecily G. is a lonely giraffe until Curious George and his family come to stay with her.

THE MUDDLE

In the middle of the muddle is me.
It's a place where I am very apt to be.
I get myself all straightened out
          And then
I'm right back in the muddle
          Again.

Marchette Chute

LOST AT THE ZOO

If I were lost
Inside the zoo,
I think that this
Is what I'd do.

I'd say, "Giraffe,
Please look around —
Your head is high
Above the ground.

"Will you point out
To me the place
Where you can see
My mother's face?"

I'm sure Giraffe
Would find my mama,
Looking at an elk
Or llama.

I'd leap to her
Like a kangaroo,
And never get lost
Again at the zoo!

Ilo Orleans

Tye May
and the
Magic Brush

by Molly Garrett Bang

1. Tye May Learns to Draw

Many years ago a cruel and greedy emperor ruled over China. His people were very poor. One of the poorest was Tye May. Her mother and father were dead and she lived alone. Every day she gathered firewood and cut reeds to sell in the marketplace.

One day Tye May passed by the school. She saw the teacher painting and stopped to watch. She knew, right then, that was what she wanted to do.

"Please, sir," she said to the teacher, "I would like to learn how to paint, but I have no money to buy a brush. Would you lend me one?"

The teacher turned red with anger. "Beggar girls don't paint," he said. "Get out of here!"

But Tye May had an iron
will. She decided to make
pictures her own way. Now
when she gathered firewood,
she used the sticks to draw
animals in the dirt. When
she cut reeds, she drew fish
on the rocks with her wet fingers. Soon she drew so
well that her pictures looked almost alive.

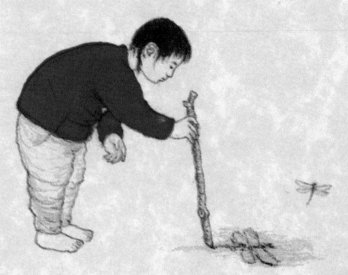

When people saw her drawings of fish, they
thought the fish would swim away. When they saw
her pictures of birds, they thought the birds were
going to sing.

But still Tye May had no brush. Every night she
thought how happy she would be if she could have one.

2. The Magic Brush

Tye May worked especially hard one day, and drew until late at night. She fell into a deep sleep. A woman appeared and held out a brush to her. "This is a magic brush," the woman said. "Use it carefully."

Tye May took it in her hands. The brush was soft and thick, and the handle was of glittering gold. It felt heavy and good. "Thank you, thank you," she cried. But the woman was gone.

Tye May woke up. It was dawn. She looked around. Everything was the same. She saw the same dirt floor, the same broken walls, the same straw mat. It had all been a dream.

But what was this brush in her hands? Tye May was lost in wonder. She painted a bird. The bird flew up, perched outside her window, and began to sing to her. It was alive! She ran outside and painted a fish. The fish flipped its tail, jumped into the river, and splashed in the water for her to see. Tye May was happy.

3. The Wicked Landlord

Soon Tye May began to use the brush to make things for the poor. For a weaver she painted a loom. For a farmer she painted a hoe, a pail, and an oxcart.

Before long, a wicked landlord heard about the magic brush. He sent for Tye May. "Paint me a picture," he ordered. Tye May refused. The landlord shut her in an empty stable.

That night it began to snow. It snowed for three days. "Now she is cold and hungry," thought the wicked landlord. "Now she will paint for me." He unlocked the stable door.

Tye May was sitting in front of a warm stove, eating hot cakes! They smelled delicious, too. The landlord shook with rage. He ordered six strong men to kill the girl and bring him the magic brush. Tye May heard the men coming. She painted herself a horse and galloped away down the road.

The landlord and his men mounted their horses and galloped after her. They were coming closer and closer. Tye May stopped her horse. She jumped down and painted a big net on the road. The horses rode into it, and the men were tangled in the ropes. Tye May tied up the net and rode away.

4. The Evil Emperor

Tye May rode on for days and nights until she came to a distant town. She decided to paint pictures and sell them in the marketplace. But she knew it would not be safe to let people know about the magic brush. She painted birds without beaks and foxes with three legs. Because the pictures were not whole they could not come to life. No one found out what the magic brush could do.

One spring day, Tye May painted a crane, and left out its eyes, as usual. But as she passed the brush over the picture, two drops of ink fell onto the bird's head.

They became eyes. The crane opened them, lifted its wings, and flew off over the marketplace. Everyone stared after the bird. Now the secret was known.

The Emperor was told,
and he sent his officers to bring
Tye May to court. Tye May knew that this Emperor
was greedy and cruel to the poor. She hated him.

"Paint me a dragon," the Emperor commanded.
Tye May painted a toad. "Paint me a firebird," he
commanded. Tye May painted a rooster. The rooster
crowed and flew onto the Emperor's head. The toad
hopped onto his belly. They flew and hopped all over
the palace. The Emperor was furious. He grabbed the
magic brush and had Tye May thrown into prison.

5. The Emperor Tries the Brush

The greedy Emperor tried to use the brush himself. He painted a big gold brick. But it was too short. He painted another. It was still too short. Then he painted a long, long, long, long golden brick, as long as the whole scroll of paper.

At once the golden brick became a golden python. It opened its red mouth and slid toward the Emperor. The Emperor fainted, and the snake disappeared. The Emperor woke up and trembled. The Emperor set Tye May free and begged her to paint for him.

He promised her gold and silver. He promised her
silks and jewels. He promised her a handsome prince.
Tye May pretended to agree.

"What would you like me to paint?" she asked.

The Emperor thought about this. He was still
very greedy. He wanted something big, but he was
also afraid. If he asked for a mountain, wild beasts
might come out of it and eat him up.

"Paint me the ocean," he commanded.

Tye May painted the ocean. It was wide and calm,
and smooth as a jade mirror. The water was so clear
the Emperor could see to the very bottom.

"Why are there no fish?" he asked.

Tye May made a few dots. The dots became fish of all the colors of the rainbow. They wiggled their tails, splashed back and forth, and swam slowly out to sea. The Emperor watched happily.

"Paint me a boat," he commanded. "I want to sail out and watch those fish."

Tye May painted a great ship. The Emperor and Empress, the Princes and Princesses, and all their court went on board. Tye May painted a few strokes. A breeze blew, ripples appeared on the water, and the ship moved off.

6. The Storm

The ship sailed too slowly for the Emperor. He stood on the bow and called to shore, "Make the wind blow stronger. Stronger!"

Tye May painted a few strokes. A strong wind began to blow and the seas grew rough. Tye May painted on. The wind howled, the waves rose higher, and the ship began to roll.

"Enough wind!" the Emperor shouted. "Enough! Enough!"

Tye May paid no attention. The winds blew into a terrible storm and drove the ship across the ocean to a lonely island. The ship crashed on the rocks, and the Emperor and his court almost drowned.

No ships came to the island and they were never
rescued. They had to work hard every day, and were
poor all the rest of their lives.

The story of Tye May and her magic brush was
told throughout the land. But what became of her?
No one knows for certain. Some say that she returned
to the village where she was born. Others say she still
walks from place to place, and paints for the poor
wherever she goes.

If I had a Magic Brush

Tye May had a magic brush that made her paintings come to life. If you had a magic brush, what would you like to paint that would come to life? Make a list of two or three things to paint. Then draw or paint the things on your list.

About the Author and Illustrator

Molly Garrett Bang

As a child, Molly Garrett Bang dreamed that someday she would illustrate books. When she was older, she moved to Japan to study Japanese painting. After she returned to the United States, her dream of becoming a book illustrator came true.

At first Molly Garrett Bang illustrated some folktales and stories her mother wrote. These books were so well liked that she started writing and illustrating her own books. You may enjoy reading her book, *The Paper Crane,* the story of a generous man whose bad luck changes when a magical paper animal comes to life.

IN AND OUT OF BOOKS

Mouse Soup by Arnold Lobel

A little mouse must think quickly if he doesn't want to end up as dinner for a weasel.

Not Just Any Ring by Danita Ross Haller

Jessie believes her new silver ring is lucky. Is it lucky enough to help get her out of trouble?

Me and Neesie by Eloise Greenfield

Janell's make-believe friend, naughty Neesie, is always getting into trouble. Will Janell give her up?

Anansi and the Moss-Covered Rock by Eric A. Kimmel

Anansi the spider is playing tricks on his friends with the help of an unusual rock. But it is his friends who have the last laugh.

Katie Morag Delivers the Mail by Mairi Hedderwick

How can Katie get into trouble by delivering mail? It all begins when she drops the mailbag into water.

Esmeralda and the Pet Parade by Cecile Schoberle

Juan's pet goat Esmeralda is always getting into trouble. What will happen when she enters the Santa Fe Pet Parade?

POLAR BEARS

Thinking It Over

How do polar bears live in the cold?

Key Words

Arctic
camouflage

A hungry polar bear comes out of its den into the cold wind and blowing snow. It runs on the thick ice until it reaches the water. Splash! The bear dives into the icy water for a long, cold swim. It swims with only its nose showing.

How do polar bears swim so comfortably in icy water? How do they run so easily on frozen land? In this lesson you will learn about the place where polar bears live and how they live there.

Where Polar Bears Live

Polar bears live in the **Arctic.** The Arctic is the area of the earth that surrounds the North Pole. Part of the Arctic is land. Part of it is water. For more than half of the year, much of the Arctic is frozen.

Animals who live in this cold, harsh place need ways to keep warm and safe. Polar bears have thick fur that keeps them warm, even during the cold Arctic winter.

The Arctic

Stop and Think

1. Where do polar bears live?
2. How do they keep warm?

What Polar Bears Eat

Polar bears get most of their food from the water. They have sharp claws and teeth for catching seals, walruses, sea birds, and fish. They hunt seals at holes in the ice where the seals come up for air. Polar bears must go from place to place to follow their prey. Sometimes they travel many miles by swimming in the water or riding on a big chunk of ice.

walrus

seal

salmon

If polar bears cannot find food in the water, they hunt on land. Polar bears have thick pads and fur on their feet to help them walk or run on slippery ice and snow. The land animals they hunt include large animals, such as reindeer and musk oxen, and small animals, such as lemmings. Polar bears can smell animals from up to ten miles away. They can even smell animal homes that are buried under snow and ice.

Polar bears do not usually eat plants. But they will eat almost anything if they are hungry, even common Arctic plants such as grasses, mosses, and shrubs.

lemming

reindeer

Stop and Think

1. What do polar bears eat?
2. Where do polar bears find most of their food?
3. How do polar bears hunt for their food?

How a Polar Bear's Color Helps It to Hunt

When a polar bear is swimming in the water it looks almost like a chunk of ice! It might hide on a real piece of floating ice and sneak up on a walrus or seal. A polar bear's white fur is good **camouflage.** That means the bear is hard to see because its white fur blends with the white ice.

A polar bear can play the same trick on land, where it blends with the snow and can surprise a lemming.

How Does Camouflage Work?

Here is an experiment you can do to see for yourself how camouflage works.

You will need two sheets of white paper, one sheet of brown paper, a pencil, and a pair of scissors.

Draw a polar bear shape on one sheet of white paper and cut it out. Put the polar bear shape on top of the other sheet of white paper. Then put the polar bear shape on top of the sheet of brown paper.

Stop and Think

1. How well could you see the shape on white paper? How well could you see the shape on brown paper?
2. Why do you think polar bears are often able to sneak up on the animals they are hunting?

Scientists at Work

Polar bears are huge animals. Many polar bears grow to a length of nine feet. They can weigh up to 1,600 pounds. They are so strong that they can kill a seal with one swipe of a paw. It is very dangerous for a person to get close to a polar bear.

So, how do scientists get close enough to polar bears to study them? One way is by watching them through a powerful telescope. From the top of a high cliff, scientists will often watch a mother polar bear teach her cubs to hunt seals at an ice hole. When polar bears are walking on the ice, scientists can use an underwater microphone to bring the sound of the bears closer.

Important Ideas

- Polar bears live in the Arctic where it is very cold.

- Polar bears have thick fur, sharp claws, and pads on their feet that help them live in the Arctic.

- Polar bears hunt mainly for animals that live in the water.

- A polar bear's white color helps it to hunt in the ice and snow.

Review

1. Where do polar bears live?
2. How do polar bears live in the cold?

Glossary

This glossary can help you find out the meanings of some of the words in this book. The meanings given are the meanings of the words as the words are used in the book.

A

activity Quick movement: *I lost my watch in all the activity of leaving for vacation.*

apology A statement that someone is sorry for something: *The boy gave his apologies for spilling my popcorn.*

artist A person who draws or paints pictures: *Mary is the artist who painted my picture.*

awful Very bad or unpleasant: *When his best friend went away for the summer, Joe felt awful.*

B

bail out To jump out of an aircraft with a parachute: *Judy bailed out of the airplane before it landed in a field.*

beam To smile broadly: *My father beamed when my teacher told him how much she liked my drawing.*

bin A large container to store things in: *We keep flour in a large bin in the kitchen.*

bin

brush A tool made of stiff hairs attached to a handle: *Beth used her new **brush** to paint a picture.*

brush

C

cautiously In a careful way: *The cat **cautiously** crept up on the bird.*

chalk A soft material used for making marks on a blackboard: *Susan used green **chalk** to draw a tree on the board.*

chew To grind or crush with the teeth: *Since mice have sharp teeth, they can **chew** through ropes.*

clutch To hold or grasp tightly: *Jane **clutched** the bat with both hands.*

come through To do what is needed: *The mouse **came through** for the lion by helping him escape from the hunters.*

copy To make something that is like or that looks like something else: *Most painters do not want to **copy** someone else's paintings. They want to paint something new.*

course The place where a race is held: *Last Saturday, there was a race on the new **course** behind the school.*

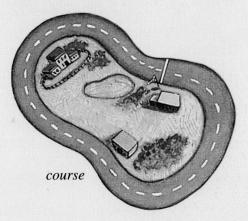
course

creature Any living animal or person: *I love to touch the wild **creatures** at the petting zoo.*

cruel Mean or unkind: *The **cruel** king made his helpers work day and night.*

cure To make a sick person well, or fix something that is wrong: *The medicine will **cure** your sore throat.*

curious Eager to find out about something: *Jeff took the clock apart because he was **curious** to see how it worked.*

disease An illness or sickness. Chicken pox is a disease that many children get.

doom Terrible trouble to come: *When I heard my sister's angry voice, I knew I was headed for **doom**.*

dough A soft, thick mixture of water, flour, and other ingredients. Dough is used to make bread and other baked foods.

emperor A man who rules a country or many countries. An emperor is like a king.

enjoy To like something: *Lisa **enjoyed** playing tag in the park.*

escape To get free or break loose: *My hamster **escaped** from its cage.*

favorite Someone or something that is liked more than anything else: *David has many shirts, but the blue one is his favorite.*

flight A trip in an airplane or space ship: *The flight took the space ship into outer space.*

foolish Silly: *The dog looked foolish with the tin can on its nose.*

fool with To play around with or take lightly: *Matches should not be fooled with.*

G

get rid of To free oneself from something that is not wanted: *We decided to get rid of the toys we didn't want anymore.*

gnaw To chew or bite: *The dog gnawed on the bone.*

grain The small, hard seed of oats, corn, wheat, or rice. The grains of these plants can be eaten or ground into flour to make bread.

grain

greedy Wanting more than one needs or deserves: *Jimmy wouldn't share the apples because he was greedy.*

guard To keep from danger: *Nessa guarded her grandmother from wild animals.*

guitar A stringed musical instrument that has a long neck and a body shaped like a pear.

guitar

hare An animal that looks very much like a rabbit. A hare is larger than a rabbit and has longer ears and legs.

hare

hind Back: *A hare's **hind** legs are longer than the front ones.*

honor A rewarding experience: *It was a great **honor** for Polly to meet the president.*

humiliation A feeling of hurt pride or shame: *The **humiliation** of losing 47 to 3 made the players on the team want to quit.*

jealous Feeling angry or envious about something another person has or is doing: *My sister was **jealous** because I went camping and she couldn't go.*

jeans Pants made from a heavy cloth: *Harvey always wore his **jeans** when he went out to play.*

kernel A grain or a seed of a cereal plant: *All the corn popped except for one **kernel**.*

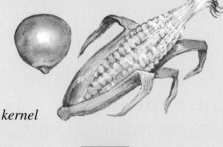

kernel

launching site The place from which a space ship is sent into space: *We went to the **launching site** to watch the space ship blast off.*

laze To lie around in a lazy manner: *The lion was **lazing** in the shade because the day was hot.*

lesson Something to be learned: *Paul wanted to be a singer when he grew up, so he took singing **lessons**.*

lope To run with long, smooth steps: *The wolf **loped** away over the ice and snow.*

magic The art of using spells, charms, and special powers to make changes in nature or people: *Ned was sure the woman used **magic** to turn the scarf into a flower.*

medal A piece of metal given to someone who has done something special: *The firefighter received a **medal** for saving many lives.*

medal

messy Dirty and not neat: *Jana's room was so **messy** I did not want to go inside.*

misery Great pain or suffering: *Gail knew that her misery would not stop until she found a way to make her brother stop teasing her.*

mitt A large, padded glove that baseball players wear: *Emily hoped her new mitt would help her catch the baseball.*

mitt

monitor A student who does a special job to help the teacher: *The paper monitor passed out drawing paper to the whole class.*

museum A building for keeping and displaying interesting and valuable things: *The guide at the museum showed us a model of a huge dinosaur.*

N

nibble To eat with small, quick bites: *Little by little, a mouse can nibble through a rope.*

O

order To give a command to someone: *Mother ordered Harry to clean his room.*

out Having lost a turn while playing baseball: *Tom was called out because the pitcher caught the ball before it hit the ground.*

P

panic To lose control with fear: *I panicked when I could not find my house key.*

parachute A large piece of cloth used to slow the fall of a person who has jumped from an airplane or other high place.

parachute

pay attention To think about something or to listen carefully to someone: *The teacher asked the class to pay attention to what she was reading.*

perseverance Continuing to try to do something even though it is very difficult: *Jay was so tired that he wanted to give up, but his perseverance helped him win the race.*

piled up Stacked or put on top of each other: *A lot of books were piled up on the table.*

piled up

potion A drink used for medicine or magic: *The woman made a potion she said would make people smarter.*

powerful Very strong: *My brother thinks his good-luck charm is powerful.*

property Something owned by someone: *These books are the property of the school.*

rage Very great anger: *The monkey howled with rage when the fox stole his bananas.*

recognize To know from past experience: *Sandy recognized her cousin even though she had not seen him in two years.*

remember To think of something again: *Pete remembered that he had to return his library books today.*

rescue To save from danger or harm: *The firefighter rescued my cat when it was caught in the tree.*

reserve To arrange ahead of time to buy or use something: *Carol wanted to be sure that she got one of the new puppies, so she reserved one before they were born.*

reward Something given in recognition of an achievement or hard work: *Anna was given a reward for finding the lost book.*

rule A statement that tells how something may or may not be done: *The rules for this game are written on the box.*

shrug To raise the shoulders to show that one does not understand something: *The grasshopper shrugged when the ant said she was too busy to play.*

shuffle To walk slowly while dragging the feet: *The bear shuffled away from Nessa's camp.*

smear To cover or stain with something that is sticky or greasy: *The new sweater was smeared with jelly.*

sneeze To force air through the mouth and nose suddenly: *When dust tickles your nose, it may cause you to sneeze.*

sniff To breathe quickly while smelling: *The dog sniffed at the bag with the hamburgers inside.*

snout A long, pointed nose: *The wolf lifted its snout into the air and howled.*

snout

space ship A vehicle used for travel outside the earth's atmosphere. A space ship sometimes travels to the moon.

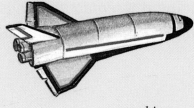
space ship

spirit Liveliness or pep: *Even though the team had lost two games in a row, they still had a lot of team spirit.*

strum To pluck the strings of a musical instrument: *Sue strummed a song on her guitar.*

supposed to To do what is expected or planned: *Ellen is supposed to practice her singing every day.*

swung Moved the arms to hit something: *Ralph swung his bat at the ball.*

T

task Job: *One task I don't like is taking out the garbage.*

tortoise A turtle that lives on land. A tortoise is a slow-moving animal that has four legs and a hard shell.

tortoise

tower A tall building or a tall part of a larger building: *The tower stood high above the other buildings.*

tower

traitor A person who is false to a friend, country, or idea.

trouble A difficult or upsetting problem: *Molly's trouble is that she worries too much.*

tundra A part of the Arctic region that has no trees and few other plants. In the tundra, the ground is frozen much of the year.

valuable Very important or useful: *A good friend is valuable.*

victory The winning of a contest or other competition: *After Elaine won the race, she celebrated her victory.*

wheat A cereal grass that has grains. The grain is often ground to make flour.

wise Very smart: *The wise woman seemed to have the answer to every question.*

wonder A feeling of amazement: *Jack looked with **wonder** as the magician performed her tricks.*

worst Extremely bad: *All of the singers are bad, but he is the **worst** of all.*

wrong Not right or true: *Nancy should have gone to first base, but she ran the **wrong** way.*

Acknowledgments

For each of the selections listed below, grateful acknowledgment is made for permission to excerpt and/or reprint original or copyrighted material, as follows:

Major Selections

The Art Lesson, written and illustrated by Tomie dePaola. Copyright © 1989 by Tomie dePaola. Reprinted by permission of G. P. Putnam's Sons. Crayola is a registered trademark of Binney & Smith Inc. Used with permission.

Best Friends, by Steven Kellogg. Copyright © 1986 by Steven Kellogg. Reprinted by permission of the publisher, Dial Books for Young Readers.

Clean Your Room, Harvey Moon!, by Pat Cummings. Copyright © 1991 by Pat Cummings. Reprinted by permission of Bradbury Press, an Affiliate of Macmillan, Inc.

Curious George Gets a Medal, by H. A. Rey. Copyright © 1957 by H. A. Rey. Copyright © renewed 1985 by Margaret E. Rey. Reprinted by permission of Houghton Mifflin Company.

The Lion and the Mouse, by Robert Hoffer. Reprinted by permission of the author.

Nessa's Fish, by Nancy Luenn and illustrated by Neil Waldman. Text copyright © 1990 by Nancy Luenn. Illustrations copyright © 1990 by Neil Waldman. Reprinted by permission of Atheneum Publishers, an imprint of Macmillan Publishing Company.

Now One Foot, Now the Other, written and illustrated by Tomie dePaola. Copyright © 1981 by Tomie dePaola. Reprinted by permission of G. P. Putnam's Sons.

"Pulín and Miga," from *Pupurupú*, by Sabine R. Ulibarrí. Copyright © 1987 by Sabine R. Ulibarrí. Copyright © 1987 by Sainz Luiselli Editores. Reprinted by permission of Sabine R. Ulibarrí.

Ronald Morgan Goes to Bat, by Patricia Reilly Giff. Text copyright © 1988 by Patricia Reilly Giff. Illustrations copyright © 1988 by Susanna Natti. Reprinted by permission of Viking Penguin, a division of Penguin Books USA, Inc.

Strega Nona's Magic Lessons, written and illustrated by Tomie dePaola. Copyright © 1982 by Tomie dePaola. Reprinted by permission of Harcourt Brace Jovanovich, Inc.

The Tortoise and the Hare, by Janet Stevens. Copyright © 1984 by Janet Stevens. All rights reserved. Reprinted by permission of Holiday House.

Tye May and the Magic Brush, by Molly Garrett Bang. Copyright © 1981 by Molly Garrett Bang. Reprinted by permission of Greenwillow Books, a division of William Morrow and Company, Inc.

Poetry

"Covers," from *Vacation Time: Poems For Children*, by Nikki Giovanni. Copyright © 1980 by Nikki Giovanni. Reprinted by permission of William Morrow and Company, Inc./Publishers, New York.

"The Dragonfly," from *Vacation Time: Poems For Children*, by Nikki Giovanni. Copyright © 1980 by Nikki Giovanni. Reprinted by permission of William Morrow and Company, Inc./Publishers, New York.

"the drum," from *Spin A Soft Black Song*, by Nikki Giovanni. Copyright © 1971, 1985 by Nikki Giovanni. Reprinted by permission of Farrar, Straus and Giroux, Inc.

"Grandma's Baby Pictures," from *Jenny*, by Beth P. Wilson. Copyright © 1990 by Beth P. Wilson. Reprinted by permission of Macmillan Publishing Company and Kendra Marcus, Bookstop Literary Agency for the author.

from "knoxville, tennessee," in *Ego-tripping And Other Poems For Young People*, by Nikki Giovanni. Copyright © 1973 by Nikki Giovanni. Reprinted by permission of William Morrow and Company, Inc./Publishers, New York.

"Lost at the Zoo," by Ilo Orleans. Copyright © 1958 by Ilo Orleans. Reprinted by permission of Karen S. Solomon.

"mommies," from *Spin A Soft Black Song*, by Nikki Giovanni. Copyright © 1971, 1985 by Nikki Giovanni. Reprinted by permission of Farrar, Straus and Giroux Inc.

"The Muddle," by Marchette Chute, from *Rhymes About Us*. Copyright © 1974 by E. P. Dutton, Inc. Reprinted by permission of Mary Chute Smith.

"The Secret Place," written and illustrated by Tomie dePaola, from *Once Upon a Time*. Copyright © 1968 by G. P. Putnam's Sons. Reprinted by permission of G. P. Putnam's Sons.

"The Tortoise and the Hare," by Tom Paxton, from *Aesop's Fables*, illustrated by Robert Rayevsky. Text copyright © 1988 by Tom Paxton. Illustrations copyright © 1988 by Robert Rayevsky. Reprinted by permission of Morrow Jr. Books (a division of William Morrow & Co.) and Wendy Lipkind Agency.

"Whistles," by Dorothy Aldis, from *Here, There and Everywhere*. Copyright 1927, 1928, copyright © renewed 1955, 1956 by Dorothy Aldis. Reprinted by permission of G. P. Putnam's Sons.

"A Year Later," in *Hello and Good-by*, by Mary Ann Hoberman. Copyright © 1959 by Mary Ann Hoberman, renewed 1987. Reprinted by permission of the Gina Maccoby Literary Agency.

Quotations from Authors/Illustrators

Patricia Reilly Giff, page 68, from *Something About the Author*, vol. 33. Copyright © 1983 by Gale Research Inc. Reprinted by permission of the publisher.

Credits

Program Design   Carbone Smolan Associates

Cover Design   Carbone Smolan Associates

Design   **8–11, 44–53, 56–66, 70–71** Carbone Smolan Associates;   **12–43, 54–55, 67–69** Fo Wilson Wylie/Studio W; **72–75** Terrelonge Design, Inc.;   **76–141** WGBH;   **142–195** DagenBela;   **196–199, 226–263** Ann Potter;   **200–225** Katherine Tillotson;   **264–271** Pronk & Associates

Introduction   (left to right) 1st row: Normand Cousineau; Toby Williams; Sal Murdocca;   2nd row: James L. Ballard; Normand Cousineau; René King Moreno;   3rd row: Darius Detwiler; Gerard Fritz/Jeroboam, Inc.; Ken Karp;   4th row: Sal Murdocca; Ken Karp; © 1988 Dan Guravich/Uniphoto Press

Table of Contents   **4** Alex Boies;   **5** Tomie dePaola; **6** Aesop's Fables;   **7** Sal Murdocca

Illustration   **8–11** Toby Williams;   **12–39** Pat Cummings; **40** René King Moreno;   **41** Susanna Natti;   **42–43** Lillian Morgan-Lewis;   **44–53** Steven Kellogg;   **54** René King Moreno;   **55** Susanna Natti;   **56–57** Alex Boies;   **58–66** Susanna Natti;   **67** René King Moreno;   **68** Susanna Natti; **69** Lillian Morgan-Lewis;   **70–71** Toby Williams;   **72–75** Tony Wade;   **78–139** Tomie dePaola;   **142–145** Normand Cousineau;   **146–157** Janet Stevens;   **158–163** Robert Rayevsky;   **164–179** S. D. Schindler;   **180–193** Darius Detwiler;   **194–195** Normand Cousineau;   **196–199** Sal Murdocca;   **200–223** Neil Waldman;   **224–225** Katherine Tillotson;   **226–241** H. A. Rey;   **242** Linda Phinney-Crehan; **244–245** Cindy Salans Rosenheim;   **246–259** Molly Bang; **260–261** Linda Phinney-Crehan;   **262–263** Sal Murdocca; **266, 267, 269, 271** Margo Stahl;   **272, 273** (left), **277** (right), **278, 279, 282** Jan Palmer;   **273** (right), **275, 277** (left), **281** Meg Kelleher-Aubrey

Photography   **72** Nancy Crampton;   **76** Courtesy of Tomie dePaola;   **76–77** Hansen/Mayer;   **94** Hansen/Mayer;   **112** Hansen/Mayer;   **136** Hansen/Mayer;   **139** Hansen/Mayer; **140–141** Hansen/Mayer;   **157** Courtesy of Holiday House (middle);   **192** Jack Newsom;   **225** Alys Carrasco (top);   **243** Photo by Werner J. Kuhn, courtesy of Houghton Mifflin Company;   **261** Courtesy of Greenwillow Books, Division of William Morrow and Co.;   **264–265** Wayne Lynch/Masterfile (spread);   **265** Comstock (inset);   **266** © Dan Guravich 1987 (bottom);   **267** Animals Animals/© Stouffer Enterprises (bottom);   **268** McCutcheon/ Masterfile (center);   **268** © Dan Guravich 1988 (bottom);   **270** Dr. Wayne Lynch (center); **270** Jack Steingrove/ Envision (bottom);   **276** Gerard Fritz/Jeroboam, Inc.;   **276** Leonard Lee Rue III/Stock Boston (bottom);   **279** Robert E. Daemmrich/TSW-CLICK/Chicago Ltd.;   **282** Gerald Corsi/Tom Stack and Associates; **Assignment Photographers**   Ken Lax   **225** (bottom). Ansen Seale   **193**.